Genevieve

Common Core State Standards

CCSS

Write-in
Literacy Handbook

McGraw Hill Education

Bothell, WA • Chicago, IL • Columbus, OH • New York, NY

Image Credit: **Cover** Wetzel and Company

The *McGraw·Hill* Companies

McGraw Hill **Education**

Copyright © 2013 The McGraw-Hill Companies, Inc.

Send all inquiries to:
McGraw-Hill Education
8787 Orion Place
Columbus, OH 43240

ISBN: 978-0-02-117085-2
MHID: 0-02-117085-1

Printed in the United States of America.

3 4 5 6 7 8 9 RHR 16 15 14 13 12

Common Core State Standards© Copyright 2010. National
Governors Association Center for Best Practices and Council of
Chief State School Officers. All rights reserved.

Contents

Grade **5**

6.3 Vocabulary Acquisition and Use

Standard
1

Lesson A
Collaborative Discussions

Working well with other people is one of the most important skills you need in school and on the job. Working with others for a common goal is called **collaboration**. One way to collaborate is to have a collaborative discussion. In a discussion, you exchange and build on ideas with other people.

In order to have successful discussions, you must sharpen your speaking and listening skills. When speaking, you should be able to express ideas clearly. As you are listening to others, you need to think about what you hear so that you can build on ideas. Then as you discuss ideas, you are able to explore and deepen your understanding of the topic.

In this lesson, you will find out more about the process for collaborative discussions, including how to do the following:

- Prepare for Discussions
- Participate in Discussions
- Respond to Ideas and Questions
- Reflect on Ideas and Draw Conclusions

Prepare for Discussions

To prepare for discussions, all participants must do their part and help one another. Being prepared shows responsibility. Before a discussion, follow these guidelines to be prepared:

- **Listen carefully to instructions.**
- **Make sure you understand what you are expected to do.**
  - If you are unsure of the topic of the discussion or what is expected, ask questions.
  - For example, your teacher says the class will discuss the Gold Rush in two weeks, and everyone needs to read up on it before the discussion. To make sure you understand the assignment, you might ask if the teacher could suggest the kinds of books or articles you could read. Write down these suggestions.
- **Plan your time.**
  - Preview what you will be reading.
  - Estimate how much time it will take you to complete the assignment.
  - If the assignment is long, break up the assignment into sections.
- **Stay focused.**
  - Pay attention and stay on task even when it's challenging.
  - To stay focused, set goals and reward yourself with breaks when you reach your goals.
- **Keep track of what you learn.**
  - When reading and studying, take notes. This will help you remember what you read.
  - You can also write down your thoughts and reactions to your reading. You will use your notes when you discuss the material with others.

Turn to page 4 to practice preparing for a discussion.

Name _____

Prepare for Discussions

Practice

Work with a group to decide how you would prepare for each of these discussion topics. The first one is done for you. Jot down notes about the kinds of planning you would do. Then have the group select one topic and prepare for a discussion on the topic.

Discussion Topic	How would I prepare?
Volunteering in Our Community	• Check volunteer Web sites for programs in the area. • Interview people who volunteer in the community. • Read newspapers for volunteer opportunities. • Make a list of places that need volunteers.
Mars Exploration	
The Bill of Rights	
The Geography of Our State	

Common Core State Standards Literacy Handbook

Participate in Discussions

When discussing topics with a partner, a group, or with the whole class, you need to listen carefully and think about the ideas that others are presenting. Then think about how these ideas relate to the information you learned when preparing for the discussion. During a discussion, follow these guidelines:

- Listen carefully to the thoughts of others.
- Review the information that you learned.
- Make connections between what others say and what you say.
- Explore ideas related to the topic.
- If someone does not understand, take time to answer his or her questions.
- Support others who are having difficulty.

When you participate in a discussion, there are rules you should follow and roles that you may have.

Rules for Effective Discussions

Follow the basic rules for active listening and speaking when having a discussion. Remember that active listening means paying close attention to what the speaker is saying. You focus on the speaker's message and make sure you understand what is being said. When it is your turn to speak, build on the ideas that others have presented and add your own ideas. During a discussion, follow these guidelines:

- Sit quietly and look at the person who is talking.
- Pay close attention to what he or she is saying. Take notes if necessary.
- Do not interrupt the speaker. You might miss important information.
- Make eye contact with the speaker.
- Take turns and share your ideas and questions with the group when the speaker is finished talking.
- Respect the opinions of others.
- Be flexible and open to different ideas.
- Make helpful comments.

Take a Look → Imagine that after carefully listening to what Derek said during a discussion, Claire did not understand everything. Instead of saying, "What you said did not make sense," Claire could say, "I'm not sure that I understood your point. Can you give an example or provide more explanation?" By asking for more information Claire is showing respect for Derek.

Now turn to page 7 to practice using rules for effective discussions.

Name _____

Rules for Effective Discussions

Practice

Use this page as an aid to discussion.

Pretend that your group gets to decide where to go on a class field trip. Discuss where you would choose to go. Remember to use active listening skills and be respectful of everyone in your group.

At the end of the discussion, talk with the whole class about how you followed the rules for discussion. If you had any areas that need improvement, explain what you can do differently next time.

Roles for Effective Discussions

Having group discussion roles can help keep discussions on track. Below are three roles that you may want people in your group to have:

Questioner

- Invites others to ask questions.
- Asks questions to keep everyone involved in the discussion.
- Asks questions to move the discussion forward.

Recorder

- Takes notes on the important ideas that are discussed.
- Summarizes key points and reports back to the class.

Discussion Monitor

- Keeps the group focused on the topic.
- Makes sure everyone gets a chance to talk.
- Reminds group members of the rules for effective discussion.

Here is an example of roles for effective discussions.

Take a Look → Suppose that a student in a group has not shared any ideas. The questioner might say, "Terri, what are your thoughts about this?" To help keep a discussion going, a questioner could ask, "What other ideas do you have on this topic?"

During a discussion, the recorder might miss some of the important information. If this happens, the recorder could say, "Can we pause for a moment and repeat that last idea?" Or the recorder can ask the group to help summarize the main points.

If the group is getting off topic, the discussion monitor could say, "I think we are getting off track. Let's think about the main topic again." Or if members are interrupting each other, the discussion monitor could say, "Before you speak, make sure that others are done speaking."

Now turn to page 9 to practice using roles for effective discussions.

Common Core State Standards Literacy Handbook

Name _____

Roles for Effective Discussions

Practice

Practice active listening and speaking skills in a group. Discuss which of the five senses you think is most important. Choose a questioner, recorder, and discussion monitor for your group.

After your group discussion, talk with the whole class about how the different roles helped your discussion. Then write down notes about how each role kept the discussion on track.

Questioner	Recorder	Discussion Monitor

Look at this example of how to participate in a discussion.

Take a Look → Suppose one group read about hurricanes. Each member read about a different aspect of hurricanes and was prepared to discuss the topic. The members of the groups took turns presenting the following information: how hurricanes develop, classification of hurricanes, and past major hurricanes.

Then the group went on to discuss how people should react if a hurricane is predicted. One student said that she read in the newspaper that people should prepare a disaster supply kit in case of weather emergencies. Another student described other ways people prepare for hurricanes, such as boarding up windows.

Now turn to page 11 to practice participating in a discussion.

Name _____

Participate for Discussions

Practice

Discuss the topic that your group chose during Prepare for Discussions (Mars exploration, the Bill of Rights, or the geography of our state). Use your notes to explain what you learned during your preparation.

- Each group member shares what he or she learned about the topic.
- Write down notes as you listen to others.
- Ask and answer any questions about the information.
- Make connections to the information discussed.

Jot down notes about what you learned from others and the connections group members made during your discussion.

What I Learned from Others	Connections Made

Respond to Ideas and Questions

Communication is a two-way process. That is, speakers and listeners are actively engaged in exploring ideas together. As the speaker presents his or her ideas, the listeners are thinking carefully about what is being said and how they feel about it. When it is their turn to speak, they take into account the ideas that others have presented.

Listening carefully and then asking thoughtful questions makes the discussion worthwhile for all. When you discuss and explore a topic, you develop a greater understanding of that topic. During the discussion, you can make connections, which can help the group come up with better ideas.

Follow these guidelines to respond to and build on the ideas of others:

- Listen carefully and think about what each person says.
- After a person speaks, respond to what has been said.
  - Answer any questions that the speaker asked.
  - Make comments on what the speaker said.
  - Ask questions.
- Build on the remarks of others.
  - When it's your turn to speak, connect to what has been said.
  - Add related ideas.
  - For example, if a speaker discusses learning how to play the guitar, you may want to compare playing the guitar to other instruments, such as the cello or drums.

Here's an example of how to respond to ideas and questions.

Take a Look → When you respond to and build on someone else's ideas, you may say something like:

- "I like that idea. Maybe we could also…"

- "I understand what you are saying. I was thinking…"

- "It's not clear to me how you connected those ideas. Can you explain how _____ is related to _____?"

- "I like what you said about…"

- "I would add the idea that…"

Let's say that a group is talking about ways to share their book reviews. One student mentions that they could create a book with everyone's review in it. Then another student responds by saying, "I understand what you are saying. I was thinking that we can share our book reviews by posting them to our class home page on the Internet. Then more people can read the reviews at one time."

Now turn to page 14 to practice responding and building on ideas.

Name _____

Respond to Ideas and Questions

Practice

Practice effective communication with a small group. Discuss your favorite school subjects and explain why you like them.

- Take turns speaking.
- Listen respectfully as members of your group are talking.
- Then give feedback on what others have said.
  - Add your own comments.
  - Think about connections to the topic.

Reflect on Ideas and Draw Conclusions

Group discussions can be a powerful way to gain new understanding. After discussion, it helps to reflect on and revise ideas. Begin by reviewing the main points. During review, everyone should check that all the main ideas are listed. Then members can add their own thoughts and views on the topic. When people review all of the information, they may realize that some of their ideas may need to change.

Here are some points to follow when reflecting on and revising ideas:

- Summarize the main ideas and important points discussed.
  - If you had a recorder take notes, the recorder can read the points that have been written down. Add any other ideas that might have been missed.
  - Include only the most important ideas in the summary.
- Reflect on your own ideas and how they may have changed based on the ideas that others have presented.
- As a group, make connections between the main ideas of the discussion and other things you have read elsewhere, other similar experiences, or something else that you know about the world.
- Draw conclusions about what is being said.
  - Use the discussion and your own knowledge to understand the topic better.
  - For example, if one person in the group says that two countries near one another use similar instruments for their music, you might draw the conclusion that the musicians influenced one another.

Turn to page 16 to practice reflecting on ideas and drawing conclusions.

Name _____

Reflect on Ideas and Draw Conclusions

Practice

In a group, take turns explaining what you enjoy doing in your free time. Listen carefully as each person speaks. After everyone has finished sharing, reflect on and discuss what you learned.

- Remember to summarize the main idea and details.
- Add your own thoughts about the topic.
- Discuss connections to the topic.
- Draw conclusions and share them.

Lesson B
Listening Skills

Just because you *hear* something doesn't mean you are listening. **Listening** involves paying close attention to what the speaker is saying. Listening is active in that you choose to focus on the speaker's message and make sure you understand what is being said. Taking notes, summarizing what the speaker said or showed, and thinking critically are important parts of active listening.

Take Notes and Summarize

You can have many purposes for listening and viewing. Sometimes you want to enjoy a song or a good story. Other times you want to learn something new, such as when you listen to a speaker, a podcast, or view a program on television. When you need to remember what you listen to, you can help yourself by:

- **Thinking about your purpose.** When you know why you are listening or viewing something, you can direct your attention to those parts of the message that are important to you. For example, if you are listening to an announcement, you pay attention to the details of the message. If you are viewing a presentation with slides, you pay attention to the visuals and the important information.

- **Taking notes as you listen and view.** Take notes by writing down the main ideas and important details. Write words, short phrases, and sentences. Use abbreviations and symbols to help you keep up with the speaker. You don't need to write everything down. Also keep track of any questions and pay special attention to visuals presented, and include that information in your notes.

- **Summarizing the information.** After the speaker is done, review the information. Review your notes and fill in any missing information. When you restate the main ideas in your own words, you are summarizing. Summarizing what you hear helps you better understand the message because you have to say it yourself and identify the main ideas. It also prevents you from copying the exact words of a speaker or writer when you restate them in your own words. Copying the exact words of another person and not giving that person credit for them is called *plagiarism*.

Take a Look → This is an example of a presentation that a listener heard.

Plants and animals are made of different kinds of cells. Each kind of cell does a certain job. For example, an animal's skin cells cover the outside of the body. Muscle cells cause movement when they contract or relax. In plants, cells within flowers make seeds. Cells within a plant's roots take in water and hold the plant in the soil.

Plant cells have two structures that animal cells do not have. For one thing, plant cells have a rigid cell wall that supports and protects the cell. Plant cells in leaves and in some stems also have chloroplasts, which are cell structures that make food.

These are the notes that the listener took.

- Plants/animals have cells that do different jobs. Example—muscle cells move, root cells absorb water and keep the plant in the ground.

- Two differences in plant cells:
  — rigid cell wall for support and protection
  — chloroplasts make food

This is the summary that the listener wrote.

Cells in plants and animals have specific jobs. For instance, muscle cells in animals allow them to move, and root cells in plants absorb water and keep the plant in the ground. Rigid walls, which support and protect cells, and chloroplasts, which make food, are two types of cell structures that plants have and animals do not.

Turn to page 19 to practice taking notes and summarizing oral information.

Turn to pages 20–21 to practice taking notes and summarizing visual information.

Turn to pages 22–23 to practice taking notes and summarizing quantitative information.

Common Core State Standards Literacy Handbook

Name _____

Take Notes and Summarize Oral Information

Practice

Tell a partner about which foods you like and do not like. Have your partner take notes. When you are done speaking, tell your partner to summarize the information. Then switch roles. Remember to:

- Write phrases or short sentences when you take notes.
- Review your notes and ask any questions.
- Summarize the main points using your own words.

Name _____

Take Notes and Summarize Visual Information

Practice

With a partner, read aloud the paragraphs and flowchart. Take notes and then summarize the information. Remember to:

- Write phrases or short sentences when you take notes.
- Include information from visuals, such as a time line or flowchart, in your notes.
- Review your notes and ask any questions.
- Summarize the main points using your own words.

Making Laws

If you are wondering where laws come from, take a look in the mirror. Many laws begin with ideas from ordinary citizens like you!

For example, suppose that your class reads about a terrible accident at a railroad crossing. In a class discussion you agree that all railroad crossings should have gates—and you decide to do something about it, with the help of your legislative representatives.

Name _____

A bill can originate in the House or Senate. Here's the path that your idea would take to become a law.

How a Bill Becomes a Law

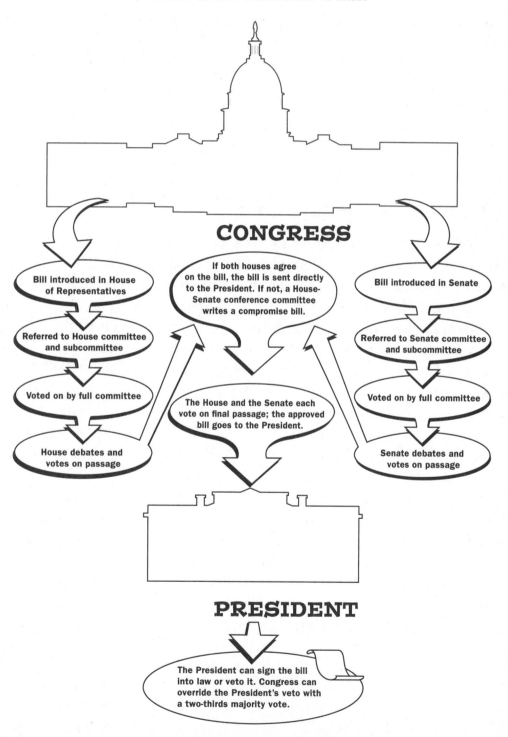

CONGRESS

Bill introduced in House of Representatives

Referred to House committee and subcommittee

Voted on by full committee

House debates and votes on passage

If both houses agree on the bill, the bill is sent directly to the President. If not, a House-Senate conference committee writes a compromise bill.

The House and the Senate each vote on final passage; the approved bill goes to the President.

Bill introduced in Senate

Referred to Senate committee and subcommittee

Voted on by full committee

Senate debates and votes on passage

PRESIDENT

The President can sign the bill into law or veto it. Congress can override the President's veto with a two-thirds majority vote.

Name _____

Take Notes and Summarize Quantitative Information

Practice

With a partner, read aloud the paragraph and chart. Take notes and then summarize the information. Remember to:

- Write phrases or short sentences when you take notes.
- Include information from charts or graphs in your notes.
- Review your notes and ask any questions.
- Summarize the main points using your own words.

How Can I Help Hungry People?

In the late 1930s, Dan West, an Indiana farmer, was working in Spain on a relief project, helping people who were suffering because of the Spanish Civil War. As he distributed cups of milk to hungry children, he thought, *These children don't need a cup; they need a cow.*

West started a program that gives animals to families in need. The program started in Puerto Rico and is now working in more than 50 countries worldwide, including Ukraine, Senegal, China, and Peru. The animals—cows, goats, sheep, chickens, rabbits, and bees, for example—provide families with the opportunity to feed themselves. Families are also often able to breed these animals and raise more of them for food or for sale. Furthermore, they sometimes can make and sell butter, cheese, honey, woolen goods, and other products.

People who receive an animal must promise to "pass on the gift." This means that they must give an animal, such as a calf, to another person in need and teach that person how to take care of it.

Today, West's program is called Heifer International. Schools, kids, adults, and other groups give money to buy an animal. Donors can even choose which animal they want to buy! These animals give people a source of food and a way to feed themselves in the future.

Common Core State Standards Literacy Handbook

Name _____

Take Your Pick!

In 2009, donors to Heifer International could choose from a wide variety of animal gifts.

Sample Price List	
Animal	**Price**
Heifer	$500
Water buffalo	$250
Llama	$150
Sheep or goat	$120
Trio of rabbits	$60
Honeybees	$30
Flock of chicks, ducks, or geese	$20

Thinking Critically While Listening

When you are listening to a speaker, you need to think about the speaker's message. Speakers often give an idea or opinion about a topic. Speakers then support the idea or opinion with **reasons** or **evidence**. Reasons and evidence help a listener understand the topic or viewpoint of the speaker.

To understand what a speaker's main points are, you need to think about what the speaker is saying. Follow these tips.

- Identify the main idea of the speaker.
  - Usually the speaker will explain the main idea at the beginning of the speech. The main idea can also be summarized at the end as well.
  - Ask yourself, "What is the speaker talking about?"
- Identify the purpose of the speech.
  - Ask yourself if the speaker wants to inform, entertain, or persuade the listeners.
  - For example, if a speaker is talking about the climate, she may want to inform people about weather patterns in an area, she may want to tell people a story about how last year was the warmest summer on record, or she may want to persuade people to be concerned about climate change.
- Identify the reasons and evidence presented in the speech.
  - Recognize the reasons and evidence that the speaker uses to support particular points.
  - Speakers will often give reasons that provide logical explanations that support their ideas. Good reasons can convince listeners that the speaker's points are true.
  - Speakers will often use evidence that provides proof that their points are valid and true.

Thinking Critically While Listening: Model

Follow the directions to listen to an audio version of the text below. Then identify the main idea and the reasons and evidence that the speaker gives.

To listen, follow these steps.

1. Type in your *Common Core State Standards Literacy eHandbook* address in your browser's address bar.
2. Click on Part 5 Speaking and Listening in the first Table of Contents.
3. Go to 5.1 Comprehension and Collaboration
4. Click on Lesson B Listening Skills.
5. Click on Thinking Critically While Listening.
6. Click on Model.
7. Click on Listen.

Change Over Time

The Constitution changes with the writing of new amendments, and it changes when our politicians and courts interpret it to reflect the needs of the people of this country in modern times. For example, in the nineteenth century and into the early years of the twentieth century, children—some younger than ten years of age—worked long hours. Often the jobs they had were dangerous. Some children worked in mines and mills. Others walked the streets of American cities selling newspapers and other items. They didn't earn much money, were mistreated, and were sentenced to lives of low-paying jobs because many did not attend school while they worked.

Change occurred slowly regarding the rights of children. In the 1930s Franklin Roosevelt signed the Fair Labor Standards Act. This act, in part, changed the ways children were treated in the workplace. Today laws regulate the ways children can work and the amount of schooling they must receive if they do work.

What is the speaker's main idea?

To find the main idea, ask yourself: *What does the author want to tell me?* The speaker's main idea is underlined below.

Change Over Time

The Constitution changes with the writing of new amendments, and it changes when our politicians and courts interpret it to reflect the needs of the people of this country in modern times. For example, in the nineteenth century and into the early years of the twentieth century, children—some younger than ten years of age—worked long hours. Often the jobs they had were dangerous. Some children worked in mines and mills. Others walked the streets of American cities selling newspapers and other items. They didn't earn much money, were mistreated, and were sentenced to lives of low-paying jobs because many did not attend school while they worked.

Change occurred slowly regarding the rights of children. In the 1930s Franklin Roosevelt signed the Fair Labor Standards Act. This act, in part, changed the ways children were treated in the workplace. Today laws regulate the ways children can work and the amount of schooling they must receive if they do work.

What evidence does the speaker give to support the main idea?
In the second paragraph the speaker talks about changes to the rights of children. *How does the speaker to support this point?* The speaker's reasons and evidence are underlined below.

Change Over Time

The Constitution changes with the writing of new amendments, and it changes when our politicians and courts interpret it to reflect the needs of the people of this country in modern times. For example, in the nineteenth century and into the early years of the twentieth century, children—some younger than ten years of age—worked long hours. Often the jobs they had were dangerous. Some children worked in mines and mills. Others walked the streets of American cities selling newspapers and other items. They didn't earn much money, were mistreated, and were sentenced to lives of low-paying jobs because many did not attend school while they worked.

Change occurred slowly regarding the rights of children. <u>In the 1930s Franklin Roosevelt signed the Fair Labor Standards Act. This act, in part, changed the ways children were treated in the workplace.</u> Today laws regulate the ways children can work and the amount of schooling they must receive if they do work.

Now turn to page 28 to practice thinking critically while listening.

Name _____

Thinking Critically While Listening

Practice

Think about your favorite holiday. Explain to a partner why you like that holiday.

- Decide if you want to inform or persuade your partner.
- Remember to state your main idea.
- Include reasons and evidence to support your main idea.

Ask your partner to write down the main idea and details that he or she heard while listening. Check that your partner identified all of your reasons and evidence and discuss any differences. Then switch roles.

Lesson A
Present a Report

Have you ever wondered how people present a research report so easily and with cool features like technology and visuals? This lesson explains how.

A **research report** presents information about a topic using facts, details, descriptions, definitions, quotations, or examples. To learn about writing a research report, go to Writing 4.3 Lesson A **Research to Build and Present Knowledge** in Volume 1 on page 456.

In this lesson, you will learn about these four steps you can follow to prepare and present a report, and how to use this information to give your own report.

- **Prepare**
- **Rehearse**
- **Present**
- **Reflect**

Prepare

Once you are assigned to present a report, start by taking a look at your written report or a report you have read to prepare your presentation. Then you need to organize the information you will share with your audience. As you prepare your speech, you can also choose to use visuals. Then you should create note cards to help you remember what to say.

Organize Your Presentation

Review your report and decide what information you want to include in your presentation. To help your audience understand and remember your key points, choose only two or three main points to present. If your presentation has a time limit, that will also affect how much information you can include.

As you are organizing your presentation, remember to consider sequence. Your presentation should have a beginning, middle, and end.

Beginning

The beginning of your presentation should grab the audience's attention. You may want to use one of these methods to start your presentation.

- Place the audience in the center of the action.
- Ask questions.
- Tell a surprising fact.
- Tell a true story.

You will also want to introduce your topic and give your thesis statement. A thesis statement tells what your report is about.

Compare these two models. Which works better for a presentation?

Written Report

In the Amazon there are water lilies that are as big as people. There are also trees that grow so thick that you cannot see the tops of them. These and more super plants thrive in the Amazon rain forest. The Amazon is one of the Earth's most important ecosystems.

Oral Presentation

Where can you find a water lily that is as big as you are? Where do the trees grow so thick and tall that you cannot even see the tops of them? These and more super plants thrive in the Amazon rain forest. Because of its many incredible plant species, the Amazon is one of the Earth's most important ecosystems.

Middle

The middle of your presentation will include more information about or examples of your thesis. Each paragraph can start with a topic sentence and then use facts, details, descriptions, definitions, quotations, and examples to support and explain your thesis. Choose two or three main points or examples.

Make sure to use transitions from one point or example to the next. Transitions are words and phrases that connect sentences and paragraphs. Transition words can do the following:

- show location (*across, around, between*)
- show time (*after, then, during*)
- compare things (*similarly, also, likewise*)
- contrast (*unlike, even though, however*)
- emphasize a point (*for this reason, in fact, again, this means*)
- add information (*next, finally, along with, another*)
- summarize (*in conclusion, lastly, as a result*)

Take a Look → Read the paragraphs below and notice the transition between paragraphs.

The Amazon River's watershed is the largest rain forest in the world. Located in South America, it stretches over a billion acres into nine countries. Because of its size, it is no wonder that biodiversity is its main feature. For example, there are nearly 40,000 species of plants there. That is more than half of all plants on the planet!

This biodiversity means that the Amazon is like a treasure chest of resources for people. You have probably tasted two of its major plant products, coffee and chocolate. Local people also grow and harvest rubber from rubber plants. Two kinds of berries, açaí and guarana, are used to make fruit juices and sodas. Perhaps most importantly, many medicines come from the plants there. One of them is quinine, which comes from the bark of the cinchona tree and helps to treat malaria.

End

The conclusion of your presentation may summarize the main points and review your thesis statement. It often helps to look at the opening statements. Look at how you started the report to help you make that connection. For instance, if you started with a thesis statement, you can ask a question about it in your conclusion and then summarize your points.

Take a Look → I began this presentation by saying, "Because of its many incredible plant species, the Amazon is one of Earth's most important ecosystems." The Amazon may be one of Earth's most important ecosystems because we depend on it to survive. In what ways have we learned that our world depends on the Amazon rain forest? We learned that living things that grow there provide a great deal of biodiversity, resources, and climate-controlling potential. From the flavors in our juice to the medicine from our doctors, the plants of the Amazon help support life around the world. They truly are the super powers in one of Earth's most amazing places.

Use Visuals

Think about the information you are presenting and decide if any visuals would help your audience. Visuals can help your audience understand and remember the main ideas and key details of your report. The list below shows different types of visuals you may want to use or create.

- **Objects and Models:** Real objects or models can help your audience understand something that may not be familiar to them. For example, if your presentation is about martial arts, you might want to bring in a uniform or belt that is worn when practicing the sport.

- **Photographs and Illustrations:** Photographs or illustrations give your audience a picture of what you are talking about.

- **Posters:** Using posters can help you show your audience at a glance what the important ideas are.

- **Charts and Graphs:** Using charts and graphs provides a way of presenting facts and data in a simple and organized format.

- **Time Lines:** Time lines can help your audience see at a glance the dates and order of events.

- **Diagrams:** Using diagrams provides a way of showing your audience information with a simple drawing with labels. For example, if your presentation is about earthquakes, you might want to display a diagram that shows what happens during an earthquake.

- **Maps:** Viewing maps can help your audience know where the places you have described are located.

Take a Look → If you were giving a presentation about plants in the Amazon, you could show photographs of some of the different plants from the rain forest. You could also show products that are made from rain forest plants, such as chocolate.

Use Technology

You might want to consider how you can use technology in your presentation. Technology can be part of your visuals. For example, if your report is about another country, you could show an interactive map. To share your presentation with other classes, you could make a podcast. You could also use audio recordings in your presentation if you were talking about animal calls. Below are some technology formats that you may want to use in your presentation.

- **Video:** Videos provide a way for your audience to watch and listen to information about your research.

- **Audio Recording:** Listening to audio recordings lets your audience hear an example related to your topic. For instance, if your report was about your grandmother's history and you recorded an interview, you could play part of the interview.

- **Slide Show:** Using a slide show allows you to display photographs, illustrations, or an outline of important points for your audience.

- **Interactive Map:** Using an interactive map provides a way to show your audience different views of an area. With an interactive map you may be able to zoom in or out. Some programs allow you to add photos, text, or audio, or show landmarks, such as rivers and mountains.

- **Podcast:** Using a podcast is a way to share an audio recording online. If you create a podcast, you can share your presentation with other people at different times.

- **Web Site:** Using a Web site allows you to show your audience additional information, such as images and videos. For example, if you were giving a report on weather, you might show a weather forecast from a Web site.

- **Multimedia Time Line:** Using a multimedia time line allows you to add images and information to the events on a time line.

Take a Look → Suppose you are giving a presentation about plants of the Amazon, and you find out that your room has access to technology. You might show different images of the plants as a slide show of photographs.

Write Note Cards

Once you have decided what information you will present, use note cards to summarize the main ideas in your report. Brief, focused note cards help you remember what to say when you are speaking. When you present, you do not want to read directly from your cards. Follow these tips when writing your notes:

- Write key words and phrases on your note cards.
- Number the cards and put them in order.
- If you are quoting a person or text, write the whole quote.
- If you are presenting facts, write down the fact.
- If you are defining key terms, write down the definition.

See the example of the notecard below.

#1

- Amazon is over a billion acres,

  9 countries

- biodiversity is main feature

- almost 40,000 species of plants

- more than half of plants on the planet

Rehearse

Practice giving your presentation several times so that you are confident about what you want to say.

- First rehearse on your own in a quiet place.
- Then practice in front of friends or family members.

The more you practice, the easier it will be to remember your speech.

Sometimes speeches have time limits. If this is the case, you should record the time it takes for you to give your presentation.

- If your speech is too short, think about adding information or giving more explanation.
- If your speech is too long, consider taking out some information.

Follow these tips when rehearsing:

- When you present, do not read directly from your notes.
- Make eye contact with your audience.
- Look down briefly at your notes to remind yourself what you want to say next.
- Speak clearly and at a pace that can be understood by your audience.
- If your report has a time limit, time your speech.

Use Your Voice

When you are giving a presentation, it is important to use your voice effectively. It is not just what you say, but how you say it. The volume, pace or speed, and tone of your voice will affect how well people understand you.

- Speak clearly and loud enough for everyone in the room to hear.
- Don't talk too fast. Be sure to speak more slowly when you explain important points.
- Vary your tone of voice so that your speech sounds natural. For example, do not speak in monotone, like a robot! It is okay to use emotion in your speech.
- Try to avoid saying unnecessary words, such as *um, ah, well*.

Take a Look → Suppose you are listening to a presentation, but the speaker is so talking too fast that you cannot understand her. She is not using her voice effectively. When you give the speaker feedback, you can tell her to speak more slowly.

Use Gestures and Body Language

Gestures and body language can help express your ideas during a presentation. How you use your eyes and hands and the position of your body are all important.

- Look at your audience. Make eye contact with them. Pay attention to everyone in the room.
- Gesture with your hands and arms to help explain your points. For example, you might spread your arms out when you are talking about something that's very large.
- Stand up straight and be calm. Avoid rocking back and forth or moving around when it's not necessary.
- Avoid turning your back on your audience. Hold your visual aids beside you so that you can continue to face forward while you present.

Common Core State Standards Literacy Handbook

Take a Look → Suppose that a speaker always looked down at his note cards and held them tightly. He did not use any hand gestures. You could suggest that he practice his presentation more so that he does not have to rely on his notes as much. Then he can make more eye contact and use more gestures. Suppose that a speaker always looked down at his note cards and held them tightly. He did not use any hand gestures. You could suggest that he practice his presentation more so that he does not have to rely on his notes as much. Then he can make more eye contact and use more gestures.

Feedback and Revise

After your rehearsal in front of other people, follow any suggestions that your audience has. They may want you to explain something in more detail or they may give you suggestions about your voice or gestures.

Present

Some people make presenting look easy! How do they do it?

It's understandable if you are nervous. A lot of people feel nervous before they present. So how can you present like a professional? These tips will help you relax and show confidence during your presentation.

- Have all your notes and visuals ready.
- Take a few deep breaths.
- Stand up straight.
- Look at the audience.
- Speak clearly and slowly.
- Speak loud enough so everyone can hear.
- Speak with excitement.
- Use appropriate gestures.
- Hold your visual aids so everyone can see them.
- Remember to smile.

Reflect

After presenting your report, you and your audience can reflect on the information and the speech. At the end of your presentation, you can answer questions from the audience. You can also use comments from the audience and your own thoughts to evaluate the presentation. Now learn more about reflecting on your presentation.

Answer Questions

After your presentation, members of the audience can ask you questions about the information you presented. Here are some tips to help you answer their questions.

- After someone from the audience asks a question, repeat it to be sure you understand what is being asked.
- If you don't understand the question, ask the questioner to rephrase it.
- Try to answer the question clearly and briefly. You want to allow time for other questions.
- Don't worry if you don't know the answer. You can offer to research it or ask the audience what they think.

Take a Look → Suppose you gave a speech on plants of the Amazon and someone asks you if any of the plants are in danger of extinction. You can repeat the question to check that you understand it. If you did not find out that information during your research, you could ask if anyone in your audience knows about that issue. If no one else does, you can offer to do more research and give them an answer later.

Evaluate the Presentation

After your presentation, think about what went well. Ask yourself what areas you could improve upon for next time. You can also ask your peers for feedback on your presentation skills. Write down what areas you need to practice more. Then the next time you give a presentation, you will be more comfortable and confident.

Take a Look → Suppose that you had wanted to show a part of a video during your presentation. You had the DVD with you, but you could not play it because the room did not have a DVD player. You learned that you need to check if the classroom has the equipment that you need. Next time you should ask your teacher if a television and DVD player are available for presentations.

Lesson B
Present an Opinion Piece

You often give others an **opinion**. Sometimes you give an opinion in response to a question, such as: *Which season do you like best?* Other times, you have to present an opinion and support it with evidence, such as with a book review or opinion essay. The ability to present and support an opinion is an important skill to have. When you present an opinion, you use facts and details to explain your reasoning.

To learn about writing an opinion piece, go to Writing 4.1 Lesson A **Write Opinion Pieces** in Volume 1 on page 281.

Below are the steps you can follow to prepare and present an opinion. Learn more about these, then you can use this information to give your own opinion.

- **Prepare**
- **Rehearse**
- **Present**
- **Reflect**

Prepare

Once you are assigned to present an opinion piece, start by looking for an opinion essay or book review that you have written, or write a new piece. Then decide on and organize the information you will share with your audience. As you prepare your speech, you can also choose to use visuals. Then you should create note cards to help you remember what to say.

Organize Your Presentation

Review your opinion essay or book review and decide what information you want to include in your presentation. To help your audience understand and possibly adopt your opinion, choose two or three strong points, or reasons, to present.

Your presentation should state your opinion and have convincing reasons that support it. As you are organizing your presentation, remember to include key details that support each reason. This will help your audience see your point of view.

Now learn more about how to begin your presentation, support your opinion, and conclude your presentation.

Introduce Your Opinion

At the beginning of your presentation, you want to grab the audience's attention and give an opinion statement about a topic. You may also want to use one of these methods to start your presentation.

- Refer to experts or other people.
- Ask questions.
- Tell a surprising fact.
- Tell a true story.

Take a Look → When you give your opinion, you are telling the audience what you think. Read the example below. The opinion statement is underlined.

Some people say that too much time and money go into space exploration. They say we should focus instead on preserving our own planet. Although I understand these opinions, I think space exploration should continue and will expand human horizons.

Share Your Reasons

The middle part of your presentation should include reasons with key details that support your opinion. Each paragraph can start with a topic sentence and then use facts, details, descriptions, quotations, and examples to support and explain your reasons. Choose two or three strong reasons for your presentation.

Make sure to use transitions from one reason to the next. Transitions are words and phrases that connect sentences and paragraphs. Transition words can do the following:

- show location (across, around, between)
- show time (after, then, during)
- compare things (similarly, also, likewise)
- contrast (unlike, even though, however)
- emphasize a point (for this reason, in fact, again, this means)
- add information (next, finally, along with, another)
- summarize (in conclusion, lastly, as a result)
- show examples (also, for example, as a result)

Take a Look → Read the paragraphs below. The transitions between paragraphs are underlined.

If we were to build a lunar base on the moon, we could expand our knowledge of the moon and our solar system. By studying the craters on the moon, scientists can learn about history of the moon and the solar system. With travel and short-term living on the moon, we can also begin to develop equipment needed for other voyages, such as traveling to Mars.

Another reason to build a lunar base is so scientists and researchers could explore the resources on the moon. There are minerals on the moon that humans could possibly use. Some scientists also think that in the future it might be possible to use the solar power from the moon as an energy source.

Similarly, space exploration has led to many beneficial inventions. For example, automatic blood pressure machines were first developed to check the blood pressure of astronauts in space. Also, the scratch-resistant coating on eyeglasses came from a coating used to protect satellites. People who have pacemakers, implantable insulin pumps, and even braces have all benefited from technology that was developed because of space exploration.

Summarize Your Opinion

The conclusion of your presentation may summarize your reasons and review your opinion statement. It often helps to look at the opening statements. Look at how you started the presentation to help you make that connection with your opening. For instance, if you started with your opinion, you can summarize your reasons and ask your readers to do something about your topic.

Take a Look → In the beginning of this presentation I told you that "I think Moon exploration should continue and expand human horizons." Imagine people exploring the resources of the moon and a world with new inventions that help people. A lunar base could be the first step for traveling to Mars. Now is the time for further investigation of the moon. People ask how we can afford to explore the moon, but it's clear that we can't afford not to. If you agree with me, you can tell others about the importance of space exploration.

Use Visuals

Think about the information you are presenting and decide if any visuals would help your audience. Visuals can help your audience understand and remember the reasons for your opinion and the details you used to support those reasons. The list below shows different types of visuals you may want to use or create.

- **Objects and Models:** Real objects or models can help your audience understand something that may not be familiar to them. For example, if your presentation is about why you like ceramics, you might want to bring in something you created.

- **Photographs and Illustrations:** Photographs or illustrations give your audience a picture of what you are talking about.

- **Posters:** Posters can help your audience see at a glance what the important ideas are.

- **Charts and Graphs:** Using charts and graphs provides a way of presenting facts and data in a simple and organized format.

- **Time Lines:** With time lines, your audience see at a glance the dates and order of events.

- **Diagrams:** Using diagrams provides a way of showing your audience information with a simple drawing with labels. For example, if your presentation is about the importance of being prepared for emergencies, you might show a diagram of the fire exits at your school.

- **Maps:** Viewing maps can help your audience know where the places you have described are located.

TIPS FOR USING VISUALS:
- Check that your visual is large enough so that everyone can see it.
- Include labels that are short and easy to read.
- Keep the visual simple, and use it to explain one idea.

Take a Look → If you are giving a presentation about exploring the moon, you could show illustrations of what a lunar base might look like. Or you could show photographs of inventions that were developed because of technology from space exploration.

Use Technology

You might want to consider how you can use technology in your presentation. Technology can be part of your visuals. For example, if your report is about how local government affects your life, you could show your local government's Web site. You could also use audio recordings in your presentation if you wanted the audience to hear part of a speech from an expert on the topic. Below are some technology formats that you may want to use in your presentation.

- **Video:** Viewing videos allows your audience to watch and listen to information about your research.

- **Audio Recording:** When you use audio recordings your audience can hear an example related to your topic. For instance, if your report was about your favorite music, you could play some of the music for your audience.

- **Slide Show:** Using a slide show allows you to display photographs, illustrations, or an outline of important points for your audience.

- **Interactive Map:** Using an interactive map provides a way to show your audience different views of an area. With an interactive map you may be able to zoom in or out. Some programs allow you to add photos, text, or audio, or show landmarks, such as rivers and mountains.

- **Podcast:** Using a podcast is a way to share an audio recording online. If you create a podcast, you can share your presentation with other people at different times.

- **Web Site:** Using a Web site allows you to show your audience additional information, such as images and videos. For example, if you were telling about the importance of helping charities, you could show a Web site that helps people find charities to support.

- **Multimedia Time Line:** Using a multimedia time line allows you to add images and information to the events on a time line.

Take a Look → Suppose you are giving a presentation about going to the moon, and you find out that your room has access to technology. You can play a portion of a podcast given by a scientist about exploring the moon.

Write Note Cards

Once you have decided what information you will present, use note cards to summarize the main ideas in your presentation. Brief, focused note cards help you remember what to say when you are speaking. When you present, you do not want to read directly from your cards. Follow these tips when writing your notes:

- Write key words and phrases on your note cards.
- Number the cards and put them in order.
- If you are quoting a person or text, write the whole quote.
- If you are presenting facts, write down the fact.
- If you are defining key terms, write down the definition.

A sample notecard is below.

#1

- space exploration ⟶ inventions

- blood pressure machines, scratch-resistant eyeglasses

- pacemaker, implantable insulin pump

Rehearse

Practice giving your presentation several times so that you are confident about what you want to say.

- First rehearse on your own in a quiet place.
- Then practice in front of friends of family members.

The more you practice, the easier it will be to remember your speech.

Sometimes speeches have time limits. If this is the case, you should record the time it takes for you to give your presentation.

- If your speech is too short, think about adding more reasons or giving more examples or details.
- If your speech is too long, consider taking out some information.

Follow these tips when speaking.

- When you present, do not read directly from your notes.
- Make eye contact with your audience.
- Look down briefly at your notes to remind yourself what you want to say next.
- If your report has a time limit, time your speech.

Use Your Voice

When you are giving a presentation, it is important to use your voice effectively. It is not just what you say, but how you say it. The volume, pace or speed, and tone of your voice will affect how well people understand you.

- Speak clearly and loud enough for everyone in the room to hear.

- Don't talk too fast. Be sure to speak more slowly when you explain important reasons.

- Vary your tone of voice so that your speech sounds natural. For example, do not speak in monotone, like a robot! It is okay to use emotion in your speech.

- Try to avoid saying unnecessary words, such as *um, ah, well.*

Take a Look → Suppose you are listening to someone explain why he loves volunteering at an animal shelter, but the speaker is not showing any emotion in his speech. When you give the speaker feedback, you can tell him to use more expression and passion in his voice to show how much he cares about volunteering. Then his opinions will seem more sincere and real.

Use Gestures and Body Language

Gestures and body language can help you express your ideas during a presentation. How you use your eyes and hands and the position of your body are all important.

- Look at your audience. Make eye contact with them. Pay attention to everyone in the room.

- Gesture with your hands and arms to help explain your points. For example, you might pretend to kick a ball if you were talking about soccer.

- Stand up straight and be calm. Avoid rocking back and forth or moving around when it's not necessary.

- Avoid turning your back on your audience. Hold your visual aids beside you so that you can continue to face forward while you present.

Take a Look → Suppose that a speaker kept her arms in her pockets when she talked and was pacing back and forth. By doing this, she made it hard for others to focus on her speech. You could suggest that she practice in front of a mirror. Then she can check that she is using hand gestures and not pacing when she speaks.

Feedback and Revise

After your rehearsal in front of other people, follow any suggestions that your audience has. They may want you to explain something in more detail or they may give you suggestions about your voice or gestures.

Present

You are organized and you have rehearsed. Now you are ready to present your opinion piece. How can you make sure you are relaxed while sharing your thoughts? Try these tips.

- Have all of your notes and visuals ready.
- Take a few deep breaths.
- Stand up straight.
- Look at the audience.
- Speak clearly and slowly.
- Speak loud enough so everyone can hear.
- Speak with excitement.
- Use appropriate gestures.
- Hold your visual aids so everyone can see them.
- Remember to smile when appropriate.

Reflect

After presenting your opinion, you and your audience can reflect on the information and the speech. At the end of your presentation, you can answer questions from the audience. You can also use comments from the audience and your own thoughts to evaluate the presentation.

Answer Questions

After your presentation, members of the audience can ask you questions about the information you presented. Here are some tips to help you answer their questions.

- After someone from the audience asks a question, repeat it to be sure you understand what is being asked.

- If you don't understand the question, ask the questioner to rephrase it.

- Try to answer the question clearly and briefly. You want to allow time for other questions.

- Don't worry if you don't know the answer. You can offer to research it or ask the audience what they think.

Take a Look ↱ Suppose you gave your opinion about space exploration. One of your classmates is interested in how space exploration has benefitted people and asks you if there are more inventions from space technology that people use. If you know of other inventions, such as special foam used in mattresses, you can give additional examples. If not, you might suggest that you or your classmate try to find out more information on that topic.

Evaluate the Presentation

After your presentation, think about what went well. Ask yourself what areas you could improve upon for next time. You can also ask your peers for feedback on your presentation skills. Write down what areas you need to practice more. Then the next time you give a presentation, you will be more comfortable and confident.

Take a Look ↱ Suppose that you handed out photographs during your presentation. When your audience was looking at the photographs, they were not focusing on your speech. Next time, you could pass out the photographs at the end of your presentation. Or you can show a slideshow of your photographs so everyone can see them as you talk about them.

Standard
6

Lesson C
Levels of Language

We speak and write differently depending on the situation. We adjust our levels of language depending on who we are talking to and what the occasion is. For example, we use formal English when we are requesting information from a business or someone we don't know. If we are speaking with a friend, we would use informal English. In this lesson, you will learn more about formal and informal English and when we use them.

Use Formal English

Formal English is used mainly in writing and in some speaking situations. This style of English has a more serious tone and is commonly used in reports, essays, business letters, and conversations with people we may know but are not close friends with.

- Formal English includes more complex vocabulary than informal English. You may use words that you probably wouldn't use in a regular conversation with a friend.

- When formal English is used in writing, sentences are usually longer and more complex than those used in an informal note or e-mail.

- People also use formal English when speaking in formal situations, such as during presentations.

- When people talk about business, they use formal language. Read the example of a phone call to a tutoring business below.

Customer:	Good afternoon. I am calling to learn more about the tutoring services you provide. Do you have a moment to talk?
Business owner:	Thank you for calling. Yes, I do have time to discuss our services. In what subject area do you need tutoring?
Customer:	I am looking for a tutor in chemistry. Do you have tutors for that subject area? I would also like to know if tutors are available on Saturday mornings.
Business owner:	We do have two tutors who have chemistry degrees. One of them is available on Saturday mornings. Would you like to set up a free tutoring session for this Saturday?
Customer:	Yes, I could come at nine o'clock on Saturday. Thank you for arranging this session.
Business owner:	You are welcome. Thank you for calling. I am sure that you will find the tutoring session helpful.

Now turn to page 53 to practice using formal English.

Name _____

Use Formal Language

Practice

Follow the directions. Write your answers on the lines below. Remember to use formal English in your writing.

Create a weather report. Write down what you would say if you were giving a report about the weather on television. Then practice giving the weather report to a partner.

_____

_____

_____

_____

_____

_____

_____

_____

_____

_____

_____

_____

_____

_____

_____

_____

_____

Use Informal English

People often use **informal English** when they are speaking to friends and family. People also use informal English when they write e-mails, notes, and letters to people they know.

- When people write using informal English, they use everyday vocabulary and sometimes include expressions and slang that is common where they live. For instance, in informal English, a writer might use the word *yeah* instead of the word *yes*.

- Informal English often uses personal pronouns, such as *I*, *you*, and *we*, to create a more personal style than formal English. Contractions, such as *it's* instead of *it is*, are also very common.

- When friends and family members talk to one another they usually use informal English. Below is an example of a two cousins talking to one another.

Mindy: Hey, Dave. I'm glad you came over for dinner.

Dave: Yeah, this will be the last Sunday dinner that I'll be able to come to for awhile. We're moving next week. I'm looking forward to having a bigger yard to play in. But I won't be able to see you as much.

Mindy: I know. You'll have to call me more. You can post pictures online of your new house.

Dave: I'll definitely call you and send you some pictures. I think the next time we'll be back is for Thanksgiving.

Mindy: That's just a few months away. I'm getting hungry now. Let's go eat.

Turn to page 55 to practice using informal English.

Name _____

Use Informal English

Practice

Follow the directions. Write your answers on the lines below. Remember to use informal English as you create the announcement.

Write down what you would tell a classmate about today's weather. Then tell a partner about the weather.

_____

_____

_____

_____

_____

_____

_____

_____

_____

_____

_____

_____

_____

_____

Lesson A
Sentences

When we speak and write, we use sentences to express our ideas. There are different types of sentences that help us express ideas and thoughts.

Sentences: Statements and Questions

- A **sentence** is a group of words that expresses a complete thought.

> *I am going outside to walk the dog.*

- Every sentence begins with a **capital letter** and ends with a **punctuation mark**.

> *Mom just got back from the store.*
> *What did she buy?*

- A **statement** is a sentence that tells something. It is also called a **declarative sentence**. It ends with a period. **(.)**

> *My favorite sport is basketball.*

- A **question** is a sentence that asks something. It is also called an **interrogative sentence**. It ends with a question mark. **(?)**

> *Do you play any sports?*

Now turn to page 57 to practice identifying statements and questions.

Name _____

Sentences: Statements and Questions

Practice

A. Place a period at the end of the sentence if it is a statement. Place a question mark at the end of the sentence if it is a question.

1. Sage missed vocabulary day because she had a cold _____

2. Did her group finish defining their vocabulary words _____

3. Sage likes to make up her own definitions _____

4. Is "Musical Performance" the theme for this week _____

5. She was looking forward to the Tenth Annual Vocabulary Parade _____

6. Who spelled the most words correctly _____

B. Rewrite these sentences. Be sure to use the correct end mark.

7. Sage turned red when she heard everyone laughing

_____

8. do you have a collection of unrelated objects

_____

9. Mrs. Page asked the students to spell and define the words

_____

10. why were they laughing

_____

Sentences: Commands and Exclamations

- A **command** tells someone to do something. It is also called an **imperative sentence**. It ends with a period. **(.)**

> *Clean up your room.*

- An **exclamation** expresses a strong feeling. It is also called an **exclamatory sentence**. It ends with an exclamation point. **(!)**

> *I'm excited to see you tonight!*

Now turn to pages 59–60 to practice identifying commands and exclamations.

Name _____

Sentences: Commands and Exclamations

Practice

Read each sentence. Decide whether each sentence is a command or an exclamation, and write your choice on the line. Then rewrite the sentence with the correct end mark.

1. Please tell me what the vocabulary words are for this week

   _____

   _____

2. Write each word five times

   _____

   _____

3. Be sure to include each word's definition

   _____

   _____

4. Playing vocabulary games is really fun

   _____

   _____

5. Line up by the board for the Vocabulary Parade

   _____

   _____

Name _____

6. How exciting it is to come in first place

_____

_____

7. Wow, that's an amazing gold trophy that Sage won

_____

_____

8. Make a list of your favorite vocabulary words

_____

_____

Subjects and Predicates

- The **subject** of a sentence tells whom or what the sentence is about.

  > ***Jessica*** *traveled to Spain last summer.*

- The **predicate** of a sentence tells what the subject does, has, is, or is like.

  > *She **practices** piano every night.*

- The **complete subject** includes all the words in the subject. It tells exactly whom or what the sentence is about.

  > ***The soft kittens*** *rolled around on the floor.*

- The **simple subject** is the main word in the complete subject.

  > *The red and yellow **leaves** swayed in the breeze.*

- The **complete predicate** includes all the words in the predicate.

  > *The children **laughed at the silly puppy.***

- The **simple predicate** is the main word in the complete predicate.

  > *The performers **danced** across the stage.*

Now turn to page 62 to practice identifying subjects and predicates.

Name _____

Subjects and Predicates

Practice

A. Read each sentence. Circle the simple subject, and underline the complete subject.

1. A brave man lived in the mountains.

2. Davy's pet bear danced in the forest.

3. The big, bad comet hurtled toward America.

4. Davy Crockett's red-hot enemy was discombobulated.

5. The beautiful Sally Sugartree married Davy.

B. Read each sentence. Circle the simple predicate, and underline the complete predicate.

6. The President received piles of letters.

7. Davy learned all the latest dances.

8. Sally climbed a 50-foot hickory tree.

9. Sally's dog howled loudly at Davy.

10. The people elected Davy to Congress.

Compound Subjects and Predicates

- A **compound subject** is made up of two or more simple subjects that have the same predicate.

> **Keith and Lynn** listened to music together.

- A **compound predicate** is made up of two or more simple predicates that have the same subject.

> Marissa **stopped and asked** for directions.

- You can combine two sentences by joining two subjects or two predicates with *and* or *or*.

> Kristen walked to the store.
> Mark walked to the store.
> Kristen and Mark walked to the story.
>
> You can buy a pair of skates.
> You can rent a pair of skates.
> You can buy or rent a pair of skates.

Now turn to page 64 to practice identifying compound subjects and predicates.

Name _____

Compound Subjects and Predicates

Practice

A. Read each sentence. Write CS on the line if the sentence has a compound subject. Write CP on the line if the sentence has a compound predicate.

1. Davy and John danced in the forest. _____

2. Davy combed his hair with a rake and shaved his beard with an ax. _____

3. The President and Davy posed for pictures. _____

4. Davy climbed to the top of Eagle Eye Peak and waited for the comet. _____

B. Rewrite each pair of sentences as one sentence. Use *and* or *or* to form a compound subject or a compound predicate.

5. Davy jumped over the comet's shoulder. Davy planted his teeth around its neck.

_____

_____

6. Sally Sugartree was happy to see Davy return. The community was happy to see

Davy return.

_____

_____

Simple and Compound Sentences

- A **simple sentence** has one subject and one predicate. The subject or the predicate may be compound.

> *Deer live in the woods behind our house.*

- A **conjunction** joins words or groups of words. *And, but,* and *or* are conjunctions.

> *I went to the amusement park, **but** I didn't go on any of the rides.*

- A **compound sentence** is made up of two or more simple sentences that are connected by a comma or semicolon and a conjunction.

> *Frogs live near the pond, **and** they eat flies and mosquitoes.*

Now turn to pages 66–67 to practice identifying simple and compound sentences.

6

Name _Genevieve   Sept. 26_

Simple and Compound Sentences 1

Practice

Read each sentence below. If it is a simple sentence, write *S* on the line. If it is a compound sentence, write *C* on the line.

1. Pakenham went searching for trees. ___S___

2. General Sherman is the name of a person, but it is also the name of a giant sequoia.
_____C_____

3. Is that a coniferous forest biome or a deciduous forest? ___S___

4. The fallen leaves enrich the soil, and the soil helps all kinds of plant life grow.
_____C_____

5. Oak, beech, ash, and maple trees are typical of a deciduous forest.
_____S_____

6. Many types of insects and animals live in that habitat.
_____S_____

Name *Sept. 26   Genevieve*

Simple and Compound Sentences 2
Practice

A. Read each compound sentence below. Underline the conjunction, and put a comma in the correct place.

1. Limited rainfall or lengthy drought can cause wildfires, but these fires can also be caused by campfires or a stray match.

2. Helicopters can drop chemicals to slow flames, and firefighters can set up fire lines.

3. Tiny bonsai trees may look like young plants, but they are fully grown.

4. Many areas in the world are covered with trees, but the Arctic tundra is treeless.

5. Moisture is absorbed, and then it evaporates and falls as rain.

B. Read each sentence below. If it is a compound sentence, write C on the line. If it is not a compound sentence, leave the line blank.

6. There are no leaves to decompose and make the ground suitable for growth.

   _____

7. Some plants will not thrive in a coniferous forest, but some animals do well in this biome.

   _____ *C* _____

8. North America, Europe, and eastern Asia all have deciduous forests.

   _____

Complex Sentences

- Some conjunctions tell *where, when, why, how,* or *under what conditions.* These conjunctions include *after, although, as, because, before, if, since, so that, until, when, where,* and *while.* A sentence that contains two related ideas joined by one of these conjunctions is called a **complex sentence.** Complex sentences have an independent clause and one or more dependent clauses.

> *I didn't talk to my sister **because** I was mad at her.*

- An **independent clause** has a subject and a predicate and can stand alone as a sentence.

> *I didn't talk to my sister.*

- A **dependent clause** cannot stand alone as a sentence.

> *because I was mad at her*

- If the **complex sentence** begins with a conjunction, then a comma should follow the last word in the dependent clause.

> ***After** the game was over, we went out to eat at a restaurant.*

- Sometimes the comma is unnecessary if the conjunction appears in the middle of the sentence.

> *You can come to the party **if** you promise to be on time.*

Now turn to pages 69–70 to practice writing complex sentences.

Name _____

Complex Sentences 1

Practice

Combine each pair of sentences using the conjunction in parentheses.

1. They tasted space food. They wore space suits. (and)

   _____

   _____

2. Gum and drinks are not allowed. They can create disasters in the dirt-free zone. (because)

   _____

   _____

3. The students were told to remove their jewelry. They would not be injured. (so that)

   _____

   _____

4. The trainer would hold on to the chair. The last student had a turn. (until)

   _____

   _____

5. He volunteered to sit in the gravity chair. He realized how hard it was to move around. (before)

   _____

   _____

Name _____

Complex Sentences 2

Practice

From each pair of conjunctions in parentheses, choose the conjunction that combines the sentences into a single sentence that makes sense. Write the new sentence, using a comma if necessary.

1. The Hubble Telescope must be powerful. It can spot a firefly 10,000 miles away. (because/although)

   _____

   _____

2. I was feeling brave. I saw how fast the multi-axis trainer was spinning. (so that/before)

   _____

   _____

3. Bethany held on to the 5DF Chair. The kids practiced moving along the wall. (while/because)

   _____

   _____

4. The moon does not have an atmosphere. There is no wind to blow the prints away. (until/since)

   _____

   _____

Fixing Run-on Sentences

- A **run-on sentence** joins together two or more sentences that should be written separately.

> *I wrote a letter to Pablo I haven't mailed the letter yet.*

- You can correct run-on sentences by separating the complete ideas into separate sentences.

> *I wrote a letter to Pablo.*
> *I haven't mailed the letter yet.*

- You can also correct run-on sentences by rewriting them as compound or complex sentences.

> *I wrote a letter to Pablo, but I haven't mailed it yet.*

Now turn to pages 72–73 to practice fixing run-on sentences.

6

Name _____

Fixing Run-on Sentences 1

Practice

Correct the run-on sentences below either by separating them into two sentences or by rewriting them as a compound or complex sentence.

1. San Pablo Etla is on the edge of a valley Lupe's father built their house on the mountainside.

   _____

   _____

2. Lupe found Pipiolo asleep inside an old shoe she saw greatness when he opened his eyes.

   _____

   _____

3. The roof dogs guarded the roofs they would bark furiously down at Lupe and Pipiolo.

   _____

   _____

4. Pipiolo slipped into a cornfield Lupe followed him.

   _____

   _____

5. Pipiolo barked all the dogs jumped down onto the pile of oranges in the truck.

   _____

   _____

6. Lupe took a walk over to the village of Viquera it was a longer route to her school.

   _____

   _____

Common Core State Standards Literacy Handbook

Name _____

Fixing Run-on Sentences 2

Practice

Correct the run-on sentences below either by separating them into two sentences or by rewriting them as a compound or complex sentence.

1. Lupe lived in San Pablo Etla the village is in southern Mexico.

   _____

   _____

2. The roof dogs would run to the edge of their roofs they would bark furiously at Lupe and Pipiolo.

   _____

   _____

3. The dogs didn't frighten Lupe she knew they were the ones who were frightened.

   _____

   _____

4. Pipiolo was lucky Lupe didn't have a flat roof Papa would have put him up there.

   _____

   _____

5. Lupe gave each roof dog a tuft of grass she saved the piece with a flower for Chulita.

   _____

   _____

6. Lupe continued to dig up grass Pipiolo slept in the shade.

   _____

   _____

Fixing Sentence Fragments

A **sentence fragment** is a group of words that does not express a complete thought. A fragment may be missing a subject, a predicate, or both. You can correct a fragment by adding the missing part of the sentence.

> *Went to the bank. (sentence fragment—missing a subject)*
>
> *Molly went to the bank. (complete sentence)*

Now turn to pages 75–76 to practice fixing sentence fragments.

Name _____

Fixing Sentence Fragments

Practice

Correct the sentence fragments below by adding a subject, predicate, or both. Write the new sentences on the lines provided.

1. Commanded the roof dogs to escape.

_____

2. Was the only dog left on the truck.

_____

3. The big truck.

_____

4. Missed the smell of her grandma's brownies.

_____

5. The tallest building in the city.

_____

6. Owns a big farm in the country.

_____

7. Marcus, Kathy, and Lisa.

_____

Name _____

8. The winning football team.

_____

9. On the bleachers.

_____

10. The school mascot.

_____

11. Is her birthday.

_____

12. Told me about the good news.

_____

Combining Sentences

- A **simple sentence** has one subject and one predicate. If two simple sentences deal with the same subject, they can be combined into a compound sentence.

> *Sasha ate a snack. (simple sentence)*
>
> *Sasha finished her homework. (simple sentence)*
>
> *Sasha ate a snack, and then she finished her homework. (compound sentence)*

- Sometimes you can combine two sentences by moving an adjective or adverb from one sentence to the other sentence.

> *Lucas practiced playing the guitar.*
>
> *Lucas practiced it **every day**. (adverb)*
>
> *Lucas practiced playing the guitar **every day**. (combined sentence)*
>
> *The president gave a speech.*
>
> *The speech was **long**. (adjective)*
>
> *The president gave a **long** speech. (combined sentence)*

- You can also combine two sentences that tell about the same location by moving a **prepositional phrase** from one sentence to the other sentence.

> *The little girl goes to preschool.*
>
> *The preschool is **in a different town**. (prepositional phrase)*
>
> *The little girl goes to preschool **in a different town**. (combined sentence)*

Now turn to pages 78–79 to practice combining sentences.

Name _____

Combining Sentences 1

Practice

Combine each pair of sentences. Leave out words that repeat or mean the same thing.

1. Dennis went fishing. His dad went fishing.

_____

2. It was fun looking at creatures. The creatures were tiny.

_____

3. Dennis studied plants. Dennis studied insects.

_____

4. Dennis used microscopes. He used them to help other scientists.

_____

5. He observed nature. He observed it every day.

_____

6. Scientists ask questions. They look for answers.

_____

7. There was a volcano blast. It was in 1980.

_____

8. They saw dead trees. The trees were covered with ash.

_____

9. Frogs returned to the lakes. Fish returned to the lakes.

_____

10. Place the slide on the microscope. The microscope is in the lab.

_____

Name _____

Combining Sentences 2

Practice

Read each pair of sentences. Combine them by moving an adjective, an adverb, or a prepositional phrase from one sentence to the other sentence.

1. Dennis walked to a pond. The pond was small.

_____

2. He worked in the lab. It was a science lab.

_____

3. He went to college. The college was in Seattle.

_____

4. Dennis helped others. He helped them happily.

_____

5. The scientists traveled to a camp. It was a mountain camp.

_____

6. Rivers were flooded by mud. They were flooded quickly.

_____

7. The helicopter flew over the blast zone. It flew low.

_____

8. Dennis found living things. He found them in the lakes.

_____

Lesson B
Nouns

Nouns are words that name people, places, and things. We could not communicate clearly without nouns. Imagine how confusing the world would be if no one or nothing had a name. In this lesson you will learn more about nouns.

Common and Proper Nouns

- A **noun** names a person, place, or thing.

- A **common noun** names any person, place, or thing.

> *building, boy, country*

- A **proper noun** names a particular person, place, or thing. A **proper noun** begins with a capital letter.

> *Mr. Rutt, Portland, Pacific Ocean*

- Some **proper nouns** contain more than one word. Each important word begins with a capital letter.

> *New York Yankees, Gulf of Mexico*

- The name of a day, month, or holiday begins with a capital letter.

> *Friday, December, Valentine's Day*

- A person's title is a **proper noun**.

> *Mrs. Baker, Mr. Ware, Ms. Brownlie*

Turn to pages 81–83 to practice identifying common and proper nouns.

Name _____

Common and Proper Nouns 1

Practice

A. Underline each common noun in the list. Circle each proper noun. Some of the words are not nouns.

(Becky)	(Shiloh)	town	money	in
trouble	family	bathroom	father	cobbler
when	skin	an	argue	(Judd Travers)
dog	(Murphy)	(Sunday)	head	porch
because	leg	minute	town	(Marty Preston)

B. Complete each sentence by using two of the nouns from the list above.

1. There may be ___cobbler___ ahead for ___Marty Preston___

2. He has taken in a runaway ___dog___ that belongs to ___Judd Travers___.

3. Marty's ___family___ likes ___Shiloh___ very much.

4. Marty's ___father___ takes the ticks out of Shiloh's ___skin___.

5. Marty wants to earn ___money___ by working in ___town___.

Name _____

Common and Proper Nouns 2

Practice

Read each sentence. Then write it correctly on the line.

1. jonah and sally ann live in the state of california.

   _____ Jonah and Sally Ann live in the state of California.

2. jonah hopes that dad will go to see dr. mason.

   Jonah hopes that dad will go see Dr. Mason.

3. jonah thinks that he can earn money by delivering papers on fridays.

   Jonah thinks that he can earn money by delivering papers on Friday.

4. If jonah finds work in town, he can pay mr. dennis.

   If Jonah finds work in town, he can pay Mr. Dennis.

5. jonah looks for work in sacramento, california.

   Jonah looks for work in Sacramento, California.

6. sally ann brushes daisy with an old hairbrush.

   Sally Ann brushes Daisy with an old hairbrush.

7. Even mrs. snow said nice things about daisy.

   Even Mrs. Snow said nice things about Daisy.

Common Core State Standards Literacy Handbook

Name _____

8. jonah asks doc mason about delivering newspapers.

   Jonah asks Poc Mason about delivering newspapers.

9. jonah's father's name is john henry.

   Jonah's father's name is John Henry.

10. By april, jonah, sally ann, and daisy are good friends.

   By April Jonah, Sally Ann, and Daisy are good friends.

Singular and Plural Nouns

- A **singular noun** names one person, place, or thing.

> girl, school, state

- A **plural noun** names more than one person, place, or thing.

> girls, schools, states

- A **collective noun** names a group and may be considered either singular or plural.

> committee, company, family

- Add *-s* to form the plural of most singular nouns.

> computer–computers   pencil–pencils

- Add *-es* to form the plural of singular nouns that end in *s*, *sh*, *ch*, or *x*.

> dress–dresses   lash–lashes
> fox–foxes   batch–batches

- To form the plural of nouns ending in a consonant and *y*, change the *y* to *i* and add *-es*.

> cherry–cherries   baby–babies

- To form the plural of nouns ending in a vowel and *y*, add *-s*.

> monkey–monkeys   Sunday–Sundays

Now turn to pages 85–87 to practice using singular and plural nouns.

Name _____

Singular and Plural Nouns 1

Practice

A. Write the plural of each noun.

1. color _____

2. pattern _____

3. food _____

4. warning _____

5. sound _____

6. head _____

7. bite _____

8. section _____

9. button _____

10. fang _____

Name _____

B. Rewrite each sentence. Correct the underlined nouns.

11. There are 30 different <u>kind</u> of rattlers.

_____

12. Rattlers can be found in almost all 50 <u>state</u>.

_____

13. Rattlers live in different <u>habitat</u>.

_____

14. Canebrake rattlers live in <u>swamp</u>.

_____

Name _____

Singular and Plural Nouns 2
Practice

A. Write the plural of each noun.

1. enemy _____

2. valley _____

3. moss _____

4. bush _____

5. country _____

6. inch _____

7. box _____

8. baby _____

9. patch _____

10. family _____

B. Read each sentence. On the line provided, write the correct plural of each underlined word.

11. Squirrels and rabbits make good <u>lunch</u> _____ for rattlers.

12. Rattlers live in deserts and prairies rather than in <u>city</u> _____.

13. The McCrystals spend many <u>day</u> _____ helping to protect rattlers.

14. Sometimes coyotes and <u>fox</u> _____ eat rattlers.

Irregular Plural Nouns

- To form the plural of most nouns ending in *f* or *fe*, change the *f* to *v* and add *-es*.

  knife–knives

- For some nouns ending in *f* or *fe*, add *-s*.

  roof–roofs

- To form the plural of nouns that end with a vowel and *o*, add *-s*.

  stereo–stereos   radio–radios

- To form the plural of nouns that end with a consonant and *o*, add *-s* or *-es*.

  potato–potatoes   piano–pianos

- Some nouns have special plural forms.

  man–men   child–children   goose–geese

- A few nouns have the same plural and singular form.

  deer (singular)–deer (plural)

- To determine whether the noun is singular or plural, look at the rest of the sentence.

  We saw a deer on the road. (singular)
  All of the deer ran away. (plural)

Now turn to pages 89–90 to practice using irregular plural nouns.

Name _____

Irregular Plural Nouns 1
Practice

A. Write the plural of each noun.

1. thief _____

2. leaf _____

3. giraffe _____

4. half _____

5. chief _____

B. Read each sentence. On the line provided, write the correct form of singular nouns that should be plural or plural nouns that are spelled incorrectly.

6. Library shelf are filled with books about brave people.

   _____

7. They may have acted to improve or to save other people's life.

   _____

8. They often acted to defend their many strong belief.

   _____

9. Women who acted bravely were often wifes and mothers.

   _____

10. They sometimes sacrificed themselfs to help others in need.

   _____

Name _____

Irregular Plural Nouns 2

Practice

A. Write the plural of each noun.

1. rodeo _____

2. photo _____

3. tomato _____

4. banjo _____

5. kangaroo _____

B. Read each sentence. On the line provided, write the correct form of any incorrect plural nouns.

6. Learning about the past is like hearing echos from history.

_____

7. Monuments and museums help us remember American heros.

_____

8. Architect Maya Lin designed a civil rights monument that is nine foots high.

_____

9. Memorials have been built to honor both men and womans.

_____

10. We can learn about brave people by reading books or watching videoes.

_____

Common Core State Standards Literacy Handbook

Possessive Nouns

- A **possessive noun** is a noun that shows who or what owns or has something.

- A **singular possessive noun** is a singular noun that shows ownership.

> The **teacher's** book is on the desk.

- To form the possessive of a singular noun, add an **apostrophe** (') and -s.

> girl–girl's   animal–animal's

- A **plural possessive noun** is a plural noun that shows ownership.

> The **teachers'** meeting was long.

- To form the possessive of a plural noun that ends in -s, add an **apostrophe** (').

> waiters–waiters'   students–students'

- To form the possessive of a plural noun that does not end in -s, add an **apostrophe** (') and -s.

> children–children's   teeth–teeth's
> deer–deer's   fish–fish's

Now turn to pages 92–93 to practice writing possessive nouns.

Name _____

Possessive Nouns 1

Practice

A. Write the possessive form of each noun.

1. sister _____   6. tree _____

2. lady _____   7. port _____

3. driver _____   8. night _____

4. friend _____   9. moon _____

5. balcony _____   10. sea _____

B. Rewrite each sentence. Write the correct possessive for each underlined noun.

11. <u>Amalia</u> idea was a good one.

_____

12. She suggested that they ask <u>José Manuel</u> grandma to let him play.

_____

13. As they planned, the girls bought ice cream from a <u>vendor</u> cart.

_____

14. The sisters watched a vendor fill a <u>woman</u> basket with vegetables.

_____

Common Core State Standards Literacy Handbook

Name _____

Possessive Nouns 2

Practice

Read each sentence. Write the correct possessive noun on the line.

1. José Manuel found the three girls note in the basket. _____

2. All the houses balconies had beautiful railings. _____

3. Both doors hinges squeaked. _____

4. Grandmas frown made them feel a little frightened. _____

5. Amalia called her sisters names to get their attention. _____

6. The girls smelled the corn fritters aroma, so they stayed longer. _____

7. When the girls got home, Mamis face showed that she was upset. _____

8. The sisters hadn't asked their mothers permission to invite José Manuel.

_____

9. The childrens trip to the beach was special because José Manuel joined them.

_____

10. Evelyns wish for José Manuel will come true. _____

Lesson C
Verbs

A verb tells what the subject of a sentence does or is. Every sentence must have a verb, so it's important to know the different types of verbs and what they do.

Action Verbs

- A **verb** is a word that tells what the subject of a sentence does or is.

> Tony **cheered** for his team.

- A verb can include more than one word. There may be a main verb and a helping verb.

> They **are watching** a movie.

- An **action verb** is a word that expresses action. It tells what a subject does, did, or will do.

> She **will talk** to her friend.

Now turn to pages 95–96 to practice identifying action verbs.

Name _____

Action Verbs

Practice

Write the action verb on the line following the sentence. If the sentence does not contain an action verb, leave the line blank.

1. Many Americans opposed King George's laws. _____

2. Sam Adams and John Hancock were two famous patriots. _____

3. Henry's father sold various items in his shop. _____

4. General Thomas Gage was the new royal governor. _____

5. In June of 1774, King George closed the harbor. _____

6. The harbor's closing stopped trade. _____

7. Henry walked by Province House on his way to school. _____

8. Only King George's ships sailed out of the harbor. _____

9. Henry's father drew the maps. _____

10. King George's top general lived in Province House. _____

Name _____

11. The students walk home for lunch. _____

12. Henry wears mittens and boots. _____

13. The soldiers dress in red coats. _____

14. General Gage's children live in England. _____

15. The children play together. _____

16. Some soldiers work at a fort. _____

Subject-Verb Agreement

- A verb must agree in number with its subject. A singular subject takes a singular verb. A plural subject takes a plural verb.

> My mother cooks breakfast.
> My mother and my father cook dinner.

- Add -s or -es to most verbs if the subject is singular.

> My instructor plays the piano very well.
> She teaches me every Tuesday.

- If the subject is plural, the verb must be plural. Do not add -s or -es to the verb if the subject is a plural noun.

> The police officers tell everyone to obey the law.

- Both simple and compound sentences should have correct subject-verb agreement.

> Tracey washes the car in the morning.
> Tracey walks to town in the afternoon.
> Tracey washes the car in the morning, and she walks to town in the afternoon.

Now turn to pages 98–100 to practice using subject-verb agreement in sentences.

6

Name _____

Subject-Verb Agreement 1

Practice

Circle each action verb in these sentences. If the verb does not agree with the subject, write the correct verb on the line following the sentence. All sentences should be in the present tense.

1. Rebels fights for independence. _____

2. The British troops destroys the children's snow forts. _____

3. Henry's father make a sled for Henry. _____

4. The soldiers break the ice in the pond. _____

5. Henry's brothers walks to school with Henry. _____

6. General Gage help the children. _____

7. King George punishes the colonists. _____

8. The children pulls their sleds through the snow. _____

Common Core State Standards Literacy Handbook

Name _____

Subject-Verb Agreement 2

Practice

A. Use a verb from the box to complete each sentence in a way that makes sense. On the line following each sentence, write whether the subject of the sentence is singular or plural.

practice	listen	camps	rides	brings	rides
ride	camp	bring	studies	listens	answers

1. Henry his sled down the hill. _____

2. General Gage to Henry. _____

3. The British soldiers on Boston Common. _____

B. Complete the compound sentences using words from the box above.

4. Henry's sister _____ corn bread and apple jam to the school, but her

   friends _____ pears.

5. The children _____ handwriting at school, and the teacher

   _____ any questions they ask.

Name _____

C. Change the verbs so that they agree with the subjects. Keep the sentences in the present tense.

1. Americans pays taxes to King George. _____

2. Henry color the maps. _____

3. Mr. Andrews teach the lessons. _____

4. British ships sails out to sea. _____

5. Henry study hard at school. _____

6. Henry's friends worries about the harbor. _____

Simple Verb Tenses

- A verb in the **present tense** tells what is happening now or what happens on a regular basis.

> Maggie **sleeps** in her own room.

- To form present-tense singular verbs, add *-s* or *-es* to most verbs. If the subject is *I* or *you*, do not add *-s* or *-es*.

> walk–walks   crash–crashes
>
> He asks a question.   I ask a question.

- In the present tense, use the base form of the verb with all plural subjects.

> The children **ride** the bus to school.
> They **sit** quietly.

- A verb in the **past tense** tells about an action that already happened. The past tense is often formed by adding *-d* or *-ed* to the base form of a verb.

> Mary **looked** the other way.

- If a verb ends in *e*, drop the *e* before adding *-ed*.

> hope–hoped

- If a verb ends in one vowel and one consonant, double the consonant before adding *-ed*.

> omit–omitted

6

- If a verb ends in a consonant and *y*, change the *y* to *i* before adding *-es* in the present tense or *-ed* in the past tense.

> cry–cries   carry–carried

- A verb in the **future tense** tells about an action that is going to happen. To write about the future, use the word *will* in front of the verb.

> Tom **will go** to the grocery store on his way home.

Now turn to pages 103–104 to practice using simple verb tenses.

Name _____

Simple Verb Tenses 1

Practice

Read each sentence. Change the underlined verb in the sentence to the correct form of the present tense.

1. Esther Morris <u>tryes</u> to change the law. _____

2. Colonel William Bright <u>agree</u> with Esther. _____

3. Benjamin Sheeks <u>postpone</u> the discussion until the Fourth of July.

   _____

4. Mr. Sheeks <u>wishs</u> he hadn't misbehaved in court. _____

5. Colonel Bright <u>finish</u> his career in Washington, D.C. _____

6. The professor <u>pile</u> the stones in South Pass City. _____

7. She <u>rememberes</u> what happened in South Pass City. _____

8. The Secretary of State <u>announce</u> a change to the Constitution. _____

9. Time <u>pass</u> before the United States Constitution changes. _____

10. Wyoming <u>give</u> women the right to vote before any other state. _____

Name _____

Simple Verb Tenses 2

Practice

A. **Complete each sentence with the past tense of one of the verbs from the box below.**

collect	change	remember	invite
pass	gain	serve	vote

1. Both men and women _____ in elections.

2. Women in Wyoming _____ the right to vote.

3. She _____ stones to build a memorial.

4. The government _____ the Constitution.

B. **Complete each sentence with the future tense of one of the verbs from the box above.**

5. Much time _____ before the Constitution changes again.

6. Many people _____ Esther Morris forever.

7. The mayor of South Pass City _____ the citizens to a dedication ceremony.

8. Esther Morris _____ as a judge in South Pass City.

Common Core State Standards Literacy Handbook

Main and Helping Verbs

- The **main verb** in a sentence shows what the subject does or is.

> I **walk** to the bus station.

- A **helping verb** helps the main verb show an action or make a statement.

> I **am** walking to the bus station.

- *Have*, *has*, and *had* are helping verbs.

> I **have** walked to the bus station.

- Forms of *be* (*is*, *are*, *am*, *was*, and *were*) can be used as **helping verbs.** When they are used with a main verb ending in *-ing*, they show action that is or was continuing. A main verb that ends in *-ing* is called a **present participle**.

> Sue **is walking** to the bus station.
> Sue **was walking** to the bus station.

- Make sure that the helping verb agrees with the subject. Use *is* and *was* with a singular subject. Use *are* and *were* with a plural subject or *you*. Use *am* or *was* with *I*.

> The boy **is looking** at the statue.
> The boy and the girl **are going** to the museum.
> You **were going** home.
> I **am buying** the tickets for the movie.
> I **was hiding** in the closet.

Now turn to pages 106–107 to practice identifying main and helping verbs.

6

Name _____

Main and Helping Verbs 1

Practice

A. Read the sentences. Underline the helping verb. Circle the main verb.

  1. Scientists have discovered global warming.

  2. Acid rain has occurred before.

  3. Everyone has learned a lot about the subject.

  4. Fifth graders in Michigan have established Environmental Awareness Day.

  5. Scientists have researched natural resources.

  6. Recycling glass bottles has saved a lot of electricity.

  7. We have begun to see positive results.

  8. Animals in the wilderness have suffered from pollution.

  9. The standard of living has improved steadily.

  10. People had believed that technology was the answer to every problem.

Name _____

Main and Helping Verbs 2

Practice

B. Use a form of be as a helping verb to complete each sentence.

1. The students _____ working to create a safer and more healthful environment.

2. I _____ trying to recycle all of my cans and bottles.

3. The world _____ risking the danger of global warming.

4. Acid rain _____ harming trees and wild animals.

5. Environmental organizations _____ growing around the world.

6. The result _____ appearing as an improvement in living standards.

7. Years ago, scientists _____ becoming concerned about the effects of technology.

8. McDougald's class _____ sending out a message about wilderness responsibility.

9. I _____ doing my part to protect the forests of America.

10. Parks _____ becoming beautiful places to picnic.

Perfect Verb Tenses

- The **present perfect** verb tense expresses an action that happened at an indefinite time in the past or that began in the past and continues in the present. This tense is formed by using *has* or *have* with the past participle of a verb. Most past participles end in *-ed*.

> The researchers **have traveled** to many countries.
>
> My mom **has seen** that movie before.

- The **past perfect** verb tense expresses an action that took place in the past before another action or event in the past. This tense is formed by using *had* with the past participle of the verb.

> By the time we arrived, the movie **had ended.**

- The **future perfect** verb tense expresses an action that will occur in the future before some other action or event. This tense is formed by using *will have* with the past participle of the verb.

> By the time the play opens, the actors **will have practiced** for several months.

Now turn to page 109 to practice identifying perfect verb tenses.

Name _____

Perfect Verb Tenses

Practice

Circle the perfect verb tenses in the sentences below. Then write present perfect, past perfect, or future perfect on the lines provided.

1. I have seen that play already. _____

2. Steve had been to that store before. _____

3. When we get to the restaurant, the chef will have prepared our meals for us.

   _____

4. When I finally finished my homework, my favorite television show had ended.

   _____

5. My grandparents have lived there for ten years. _____

6. Lisa has danced in many recitals. _____

7. By the time Jose got to the soccer field, the game had begun. _____

8. If we don't leave now, class will have started by the time I get to school.

   _____

9. I have eaten many different types of food. _____

10. The team had lost games before. _____

Progressive Verb Forms

- The **present progressive** form of a verb includes the helping verb *am, is,* or *are* and a main verb ending in *-ing.* This form of the present tense describes an ongoing action that is happening at the same time the statement is written.

> The students **are studying** for the test.

- The **past progressive** form of a verb includes the helping verb *was* or *were* and a main verb ending in *-ing.* This form of the past tense describes a past action that was happening when another action occurred.

> The principal **was making** an announcement when I arrived at school.

- The **future progressive** form of a verb includes the helping verbs *will be* or *shall be* and a main verb ending in *-ing.* This form of the future tense describes an ongoing or continuous action that will take place in the future.

> The fireman **will be talking** to our class this afternoon.

Now turn to page 111 to practice identifying and writing progressive verb forms.

Name _____

Progressive Verb Forms

Practice

A. Circle the progressive verb forms in the sentences below. Then write *present progressive, past progressive,* or *future progressive* on the lines provided.

1. The veterinarian is examining the injured dog. _____

2. Dr. Jones will be presenting his research next week. _____

3. The nurse was explaining what would happen in the exam room when the doctor walked in. _____

4. Susan will be joining our class tomorrow. _____

5. I am helping my sister study for her test. _____

B. Read the sentences below. Change the underlined verb in each sentence to the correct progressive form.

6. The choir was performing new songs at the concert next week. _____

7. Before I started taking Spanish classes, I am thinking about signing up for German classes. _____

8. I cannot read because my sister will be playing video games in the next room. _____

9. Our team is winning until the other team brought in their best pitcher. _____

10. In May, my family was traveling to India to visit our relatives. _____

Avoid Shifts in Verb Tense

- The tense of a verb shows the time in which the action of a sentence takes place. Shifting between verb tenses while writing causes confusion for your readers because they don't know which tense is correct or accurate.

> Incorrect: *Yesterday I made a pizza, and it tastes good.*
> (made *is in past tense;* tastes *is in present tense*)
>
> Correct: *Yesterday I made a pizza, and it tasted good.*
> (made *and* tasted *are both in past tense*)

- Tense should remain consistent. Avoid **shifts in verb tenses**. Verbs in a sentence or a paragraph should always be in the same tense. For example, both verbs in a sentence are either present tense or past tense.

> Incorrect: *Julie walked to the movie theater and waits for her friends to arrive.* (shift from past tense to present tense)
>
> Correct: *Julie walked to the movie theater and waited for her friends to arrive.* (both verbs in the past tense)

Now turn to page 113 to practice using the same verb tenses within sentences.

Name _____

Avoid Shifts in Verb Tense

Practice

A. Circle the correct form of the verbs in the parentheses ( ) below.

1. Everyone at the party danced and (sing/sang).

2. The congressman (walked/walks) around and greets his supporters.

3. Molly (comes/came) over to my desk and asked to borrow a pencil.

4. I took off my shoes before I (entered/enter) the house.

5. The baby screamed and (cries/cried) for a long time.

B. Complete each sentence below by writing a verb in the correct tense on the lines provided.

6. We cheered and _____ at the baseball game.

7. Maria _____ to the shopping center and bought new clothes.

8. Steve finished his book report and then _____ his friend.

9. Nora draws and _____ beautiful pictures.

10. Every morning, John _____ for a half mile and lifts weights.

Irregular Verbs

- An **irregular verb** is a verb that does not add -*d* or -*ed* to form the past tense.

buy–bought	bring–brought
keep–kept	swim–swam
make–made	lay–laid
sleep–slept	sell–sold

- The verbs *be* and *have* have irregular spellings for the present and past tenses.

Present Tense	**Past Tense**
am, is, are	was, were
has, have	had

- Some **irregular verbs** have special spellings when used with the helping verbs *have*, *has*, or *had*.

> We have eaten a lot of vegetables.

Now turn to pages 115–116 to practice writing irregular verbs.

Name _____

Irregular Verbs 1

Practice

Rewrite these sentences. Change all of the incorrect verbs to their correct past tense forms.

1. Danny finded a game in the park.

_____

2. The meteorite maked a huge hole in the ceiling.

_____

3. Walter and Danny flied into outer space.

_____

4. Danny throwed the ball at his brother.

_____

5. The boys weared pirate costumes to the party.

_____

6. The scuba diver rised out of the water.

_____

7. The spaceship gived off a faint glow.

_____

8. They runned away from the strange vehicle.

_____

Name _____

Irregular Verbs 2

Practice

Change the following verbs so that they can be used with the helping verb *have*, *has*, or *had*.

1. begin   had _____

2. choose   have _____

3. eat   has _____

4. drink   had _____

5. take   have _____

6. get   has _____

7. speak   had _____

8. grow   has _____

9. fly   have _____

10. know   had _____

Linking Verbs

- A **linking verb** does not show action. A linking verb shows a state of being or states a condition.

> *The pie **tastes** sweet.*

- Common linking verbs are *am, is, are, was, were, will be, seem, appear, look, taste, feel,* and *felt.*

> *I **am** cold.*
> *She **felt** sick.*

- A linking verb links the subject to a noun or an adjective in the predicate. The noun that follows a linking verb renames or identifies the subject. The adjective that follows a linking verb describes the subject. Subjects and linking verbs must agree in number.

> *That **is** Sarah. (The noun Sarah identifies the subject That.)*
> *The dog **is** big. (The adjective big describes the subject dog.)*

Now turn to pages 118–119 to practice identifying and writing linking verbs.

6

Name _____

Linking Verbs 1

Practice

A. Draw one line under the subject of each sentence. Draw two lines under the linking verb in each sentence.

1. Fatima was the first user of the water pump.

2. The people of the village are excited.

3. The water tasted very good.

4. I am proud of my grandmother.

5. We were amazed by the new invention.

B. Write the correct form of the linking verb be on the line beside each sentence.

6. My grandmother always (was, am) strong. _____

7. The people of the village (was, were) mean to my grandmother. _____

8. The baobab tree (are, is) a great resource for water. _____

9. I (is, am) a hard worker. _____

10. You (are, is) extremely smart. _____

Common Core State Standards Literacy Handbook

Name _____

Linking Verbs 2
Practice

A. Read each sentence. Underline the word that is connected to the subject by a linking verb.

1. The water pump is broken.

2. My grandmother is worried about the baobab trees.

3. I felt proud of my grandmother's accomplishment.

4. The village was concerned about the lack of water.

5. People in our village seem thankful for my grandmother's generosity.

B. Complete each sentence with a linking verb. Then underline the word or words that name or describe the subject.

6. The desert _____ a dry, hot landscape.

7. I _____ grateful for the baobab trees.

8. All of the villagers _____ fascinated with new technology.

9. I _____ a little nervous when no water spilled from the pump.

10. Water _____ better from the baobab tree.

Lesson D

Pronouns

Pronouns are words that take the place of one or more nouns. There are different types of pronouns that should be used in different situations.

Pronouns and Antecedents

- A **pronoun** is a word that takes the place of one or more nouns. A pronoun may be singular or plural.

> *Mike likes tacos.*
> ***He*** *likes tacos.*
>
> *Nancy and Kay like orange juice.*
> ***They*** *like orange juice.*

- The antecedent of a pronoun is the noun (or nouns) to which a pronoun refers. A pronoun must match its **antecedent**.

> ***Oliver and Cody*** *don't like going to the grocery store.* ***They*** *think it's boring.*

- A singular noun takes a **singular pronoun**. Singular pronouns are *I, you, he, she, it, me, him,* and *her.*

> *There is a new* **girl** *at school. I am going to talk to* **her** *tomorrow.*

• A plural noun takes a **plural pronoun**. Plural pronouns are *we, you, they, us,* and *them.*

> There are two new students at **school.** I am going to talk to **them** tomorrow.

• If a pronoun refers to more than one singular noun, the pronoun is plural.

> The **boy** and the **girl** stood in line. I asked if I could stand next to **them**.

Now turn to pages 122–124 to practice matching pronouns and antecedents.

6

Name _____

Pronouns and Antecedents 1

Practice

A. On the lines following the sentences, write the antecedents for the underlined pronouns.

1. Tricia Ann was excited because <u>she</u> was going someplace special.

   _____

2. "Someplace Special" is important to Tricia Ann; <u>it</u> is her favorite spot.

   _____

3. Mama Frances said to Tricia Ann, "Act like <u>you</u> belong to somebody."

   _____

4. People got on the bus. <u>They</u> were carrying bags of fruits and vegetables.

   _____

5. A little boy approached Tricia Ann and said that <u>he</u> was six years old.

   _____

Common Core State Standards Literacy Handbook

Name _____

**B. Read the sentences below. If the underlined pronoun is correct, write "C."
If the pronoun is incorrect, write the correct pronoun.**

6. Tricia Ann said that <u>her</u> was ready to go out by herself.

_____

7. When Tricia Ann and Mama Frances rode the bus, <u>she</u> had to sit in the back.

_____

8. At the market, Tricia Ann met Mrs. Grannell. <u>She</u> was a friend of Mama Frances.

_____

9. The bus stopped in the street; <u>he</u> was having engine trouble.

_____

10. Jimmy Lee gave Tricia Ann a pretzel, and then <u>they</u> pointed to a sign in Monroe's restaurant.

_____

Name _____

Pronouns and Antecedents 2

Practice

Complete each sentence by writing the correct pronoun.

1. "Hurry up," said Mama Frances, "before _____ change my mind."

2. Tricia Ann blew her grandmother a kiss, and then _____ rushed out the door.

3. Mama Frances told Tricia Ann, "Those signs can tell _____ where to sit, but _____ can't tell _____ what to think."

4. _____ am going to Someplace Special," thought Tricia Ann as _____ looked out the window.

5. No seats were left in the rear of the bus. _____ had been taken by the crowd of people who got on at the Farmer's Market.

6. Mrs. Grannell and Tricia Ann don't like the Jim Crow laws._____ think the laws are unfair.

7. Jimmy Lee's brother works in Monroe's Restaurant, where _____ is a cook.

8. Tricia Ann bought a soda; _____ helped wash down Jimmy Lee's pretzel.

9. When Mr. Willis referred to Tricia Ann as an angel, _____ smiled at _____ and said, "No sir. It's just _____."

10. The hotel manager said to Tricia Ann, "What makes _____ think that _____ can come inside?"

Common Core State Standards Literacy Handbook

Subject and Object Pronouns

- Use a **subject pronoun** as the subject of a sentence or to rename a noun that follows a form of the verb *to be*. The words *I, you, he, she, it, we,* and *they* are subject pronouns.

  > **We** went to the soccer field.
  >
  > The person in the picture is **I**.

- Use an **object pronoun** after an action verb or after a preposition, such as *for, at, of, with,* or *to.* The words *me, you, him, her, it, us,* and *them* are object pronouns.

  > Luke kicked the ball to **me**.
  >
  > Give **us** the ball.

- Use a **relative pronoun** at the beginning of a dependent clause. The words *that, which, who, whom,* and *whose* are relative pronouns.

  > Here is the book **that** I read last summer.

- Use an **indefinite pronoun** to refer to a non-specific subject or object. The words *one, anyone, somebody, someone, everyone, nothing,* and *each* are indefinite pronouns.

  > There are enough pencils for **everyone** in the class.

Now turn to pages 126–127 to practice using subject and object pronouns.

6

Name _____

Subject and Object Pronouns 1

Practice

Read each sentence. Write the correct subject, object, relative, or indefinite pronoun on the line.

1. Carlos and Gloria are friends. _____ have known each other for a long time.

2. When Gloria's two friends were little, Gloria's mother placed _____ on the kitchen table.

3. Gloria watched television as _____ made tortillas.

4. Now Carlos wanted Gloria to pay to attention to _____.

5. When I need help I call my Uncle Jerry. _____ is the smartest person I know.

6. At the ice cream store, I ordered two scoops of strawberry. _____ is my favorite flavor.

7. I ordered plenty of pizza, so there will be enough for _____.

8. _____ knocked on my door, so I answered it.

Name _____

Subject and Object Pronouns 2

Practice

Correct each sentence by writing the correct pronoun on the line. Then write whether the pronoun is a subject or object pronoun.

1. As Carlos and Gloria walked down the road, them saw Dos Dedos.

_____

2. "Me will catch Dos Dedos," Carlos said. _____

3. Carlos's clothes smelled terrible; in fact, the smell of they was unbearable.

_____

4. When his mother came into the kitchen, her noticed the smell. _____

5. Carlos did not want to talk about the smell, so him slipped out the back door.

_____

6. Carlos picked tomatoes from the garden and squeezed they into the bathtub.

_____

7. Him scrubbed with a cloth soaked in tomato juice. _____

8. The next day, Carlos went to church; him sat near the back. _____

9. Carlos was embarrassed by the smell of his shoes; everyone in church could smell they.

_____

10. At dinner, his parents said, "Us think Carlos is unusually quiet." _____

Reflexive Pronouns

- Use a **reflexive pronoun** instead of an object pronoun if the subject of the sentence is doing the action himself or herself. The words *myself*, *yourself, himself, herself, itself, ourselves, yourselves,* and *themselves* are reflexive pronouns.

> You can look at **yourself** in the mirror.

Now turn to page 129 to practice using reflexive pronouns.

Name _____

Reflexive Pronouns

Practice

Fill in the blanks in the sentences below with the correct reflexive pronoun.

1. You can go to the store _____.

2. My little sister can't dress _____.

3. Tom and Jen are picking up a salad for _____.

4. He made _____ sick by eating too much food.

5. Let's get _____ a treat for working so hard.

6. Girls, please get _____ ready for breakfast.

7. I shut the front door and accidentally locked _____ out of the house.

8. The little girl picked _____ up after she fell down.

9. I tried to reach the top shelf _____.

10. Look at _____! You're covered in mud!

11. Michelle looked at _____ in the mirror.

12. We can clean up the park _____.

13. My grandmother still does all of the cooking _____.

14. I don't like going in the basement by _____.

15. You can help _____ to some juice.

Pronoun-Verb Agreement

- A **present-tense** verb must agree with its **subject pronoun**.

> **She works** at the library.

- Add *-s* or *-es* to most action verbs when you use the pronouns *he*, *she*, and *it*.

> **He plays** the guitar.
> **She practices** her speech.

- Do not add *-s* or *-es* to an action verb in the present tense when you use the pronouns *I*, *we*, *you*, and *they*.

> **They attend** every meeting.

- The verbs *have* and *be* have special forms in the present tense. Make sure to use the form that agrees with the subject of the sentence.

Have	
I have	We have
You have	You have
He/She/It has	They have

Be	
I am	We are
You are	You are
He/She/It is	They are

Now turn to pages 131–133 to practice using the correct forms of verbs.

Name _____

Pronoun-Verb Agreement 1

Practice

Read each sentence. On the lines provided, write the correct form of each incorrect verb.

1. John Pike walks around Las Vegas as he ask his neighbors to vote. _____

2. He believe that voting is important. _____

3. As citizens in a democracy, we agrees. _____

4. It form the basis of our system of government. _____

5. A famous musician is giving a concert because she, too, think that voting is important.

   _____

6. She want to encourage all citizens to vote. _____

7. Political groups are active; they tries to register new voters. _____

8. Members of these groups go to concerts where they meets young people who can vote.

   _____

9. All United States citizens can vote when they turns eighteen. _____

10. Does you think that voting is important? _____

Name _____

Pronoun-Verb Agreement 2

Practice

Rewrite each sentence. Correct all errors in pronoun-verb agreement.

1. Our country has two major political parties; they is the Democratic party and the Republican party.

_____

_____

2. They has animals that represent each party.

_____

_____

3. The Democrats have their animal; it are a donkey.

_____

_____

4. The Republicans have theirs, too; it am an elephant.

_____

_____

5. The donkey is associated with Andrew Jackson; it be a symbol of strong will.

_____

_____

Name _____

6. Cartoonist Thomas Nast made the symbols famous; they is in his cartoons.

_____

_____

7. Republicans like the elephant, and they has said it is a symbol of strength and dignity.

_____

_____

8. Democrats like their donkey because it are smart and brave.

_____

_____

Possessive Pronouns

- A **possessive pronoun** shows who or what owns something. It may take the place of a possessive noun.

> This is **my** purse.
>
> That wallet is Jerry's. That wallet is **his.**

- Some **possessive pronouns** are used before nouns (*my, your, his, her, its, our, their*).

> That is **her** car.

- Some **possessive pronouns** stand alone in a sentence and function as nouns (*mine, yours, his, hers, its, ours, theirs*).

> That backpack is **mine.**

Now turn to pages 135–136 to practice using possessive pronouns.

Name _____

Possessive Pronouns 1

Practice

Read each sentence. Fill in the missing possessive pronoun.

1. _____ English word *hurricane* comes from people who lived in the tropics long ago.

2. The ancient Mayan people called _____ storm god Hunraken, and an evil Taino god was called Huracan.

3. Possibly _____ name or Hunraken's is the source of hurricane.

4. A hurricane is the strongest type of tropical storm; _____ winds blow at speeds of 74 miles an hour or more.

5. I am glad that _____ cousin Frances lives in an area that has no hurricanes; her house will not be in danger.

6. If you live in an area that does have hurricanes, keep _____ emergency supplies handy.

7. We keep _____ in the back of the big closet in my brother's room.

8. We keep a flashlight, a radio, food, and bottled water in _____ emergency kit.

9. When my mom heard news of a hurricane watch, she left _____ office to come home early.

10. The more we learn about hurricanes, the better _____ chances of coming through them safely.

Name _____

Possessive Pronouns 2

Practice

Read each sentence. Find the incorrect possessive pronoun and write it correctly on the line.

1. What kinds of storms do you have in yours town? _____

2. In my, there are hurricanes. _____

3. Mine home is located near the coast of North Carolina. _____

4. Hurricane Fran caused a lot of damage to ours house. _____

5. During the last hurricane, my sister was frightened when strong winds broke a window

   in hers room. _____

6. Many large trees fell in Phil and Gina's yard and ruined theirs shed.

   _____

7. Three big trees fell on top of the shed, crashing through her roof. _____

8. However, the roof on ours house was not damaged. _____

9. We have learned about hurricanes in mine science class. _____

10. The people in ours neighborhood help one another when hurricanes hit.

    _____

Common Core State Standards Literacy Handbook

Relative Pronouns

- A **relative pronoun** introduces a dependent clause that describes a noun or a pronoun.

> Here are the boots **that** I wore hiking.

- A **relative pronoun** *relates* to another noun that comes before it in a sentence. There are five main **relative pronouns**: *that, which, who, whom,* and *whose.*

> I can't find a book **that** contains the information I need.

- Use *that* to introduce a dependent clause that includes information that is necessary to an understanding of the sentence. Do not use a comma with *that.*

> The monument **that** we visited is in New York.

- Use *which* to introduce a dependent clause that includes information that is not essential to understand the sentence. Use a comma before *which.*

> The monument, **which** is in New York, is huge.

- Use *who* when the relative pronoun relates to the subject of the sentence. If you can replace the relative pronoun with the personal pronoun *he* or *she,* use the relative pronoun *who.*

> Jane is the girl who **won** the prize.
> **She** won the prize.

6

- Use **whom** when the relative pronoun relates to the object of the sentence. If you can replace the relative pronoun with the personal pronoun *him* or *her*, use the relative pronoun **whom**.

> Cary **whom** I met at camp last summer is coming to visit me.
>
> I met **her** at camp last summer.

Now turn to page 139 to practice using relative pronouns.

Name _____

Relative Pronouns

Practice

A. Circle the relative pronoun in each of the sentences below.

1. Steve didn't know who took the keys.

2. Laura's aunt whom I was talking with is from Alaska.

3. The book that was released last week is selling well.

4. That is the girl who won the prize.

5. Jenny wrote the letter that got published.

B. Complete each sentence below by writing the correct relative pronoun on the lines provided.

6. The tree _____ we planted is small.

7. This is the store _____ sells decorations for every holiday.

8. I don't know many people _____ have visited other countries.

9. They are the children _____ parents helped build the school.

10. The book, _____ I read in one day, was excellent.

Pronouns, Contractions, and Homophones

- **Homophones** are words that sound the same but have different spellings and meanings. *Two*, *to*, and *too* are homophones.

> I have **two** dogs.
>
> I went **to** the store.
>
> You're being **too** loud.

- *Its*, *their*, and *your* are **possessive pronouns**. *It's*, *they're*, and *you're* are **contractions** for *it is*, *they are*, and *you are*. These possessive pronouns and contractions are homophones. Be careful not to confuse possessive pronouns with contractions that sound the same.

> That is **their** boat.
>
> **They're** going sailing today.
>
> Here is **your** coat.
>
> **You're** supposed to leave in ten minutes.

- Contractions always use **apostrophes**.

> **They're** going to meet us later.
>
> **It's** going to be a fun night.
>
> **You're** not supposed to tell anyone about the surprise party.

Now turn to pages 141–143 to practice using pronouns, contractions, and homophones.

Name _____

Pronouns, Contractions, and Homophones 1

Practice

Read each sentence. The underlined pronouns and contractions are used incorrectly. Write the correct pronoun or contraction on the line.

1. Do you think <u>your</u> ready for the story? _____

2. Clap <u>you're</u> hands twice. _____

3. <u>Its</u> a story about a fisher who plays a trick on some people. _____

4. At first <u>their</u> fooled, but then they trick the fisher. _____

5. <u>Its</u> a bad day for the fisher because he has not caught any fish to sell.

   _____

6. He tricks people into leaving <u>they're</u> wares on the other side of the river.

   _____

7. <u>Their</u> afraid of falling into the river because the log bridge is shaky.

   _____

8. <u>They're</u> swimming skills are not very good. _____

9. "Leave some baskets before you cross; <u>its</u> the only way to do it," the fisher tells the

   basketmaker. _____

10. The fisher promises to hold the unsteady log in <u>it's</u> place. _____

Name _____

Pronouns, Contractions, and Homophones 2

Practice

Rewrite each sentence. Use possessive pronouns, homophones, and contractions correctly.

1. The fisher tricks some people on there way to the market.

   _____

2. He stands their next to the log bridge and shakes it.

   _____

3. There likely to be frightened by the shaky log.

   _____

4. They will think that their going to fall into the river.

   _____

5. They could lose there merchandise or even drown.

   _____

Name _____

6. "Put some of you're baskets down before you cross," the fisher says.

_____

7. He tells the others to leave some of there food before crossing the log.

_____

8. As they go to the market, there easily tricked.

_____

9. However, on they're way home, they see nothing wrong with the bridge.

_____

10. They decide that there going to trick the fisher.

_____

Lesson E
Adjectives

We use adjectives to tell more about nouns and pronouns. Adjectives help make our language more descriptive by letting us know what a noun or pronoun looks, sounds, smells, tastes, or feels like.

Adjectives

- **Adjectives** are words that describe nouns or pronouns. For example, adjectives may tell what a noun or pronoun looks, sounds, smells, tastes, or feels like. They may also describe something's purpose (for example, *sleeping* bag).

- **Adjectives** may be placed before a noun or pronoun.

> He has a **black** cat.

- **Adjectives** may be placed after the words *a*, *an*, and *the*.

> The dog has **a long** tail.

- **Adjectives** may follow a linking verb.

> My sister is **short.**

Now turn to page 145 to practice using adjectives.

Name _____

Adjectives

Practice

Read the sentences below. Circle the adjective in each sentence. Draw a line under the noun it describes. Some sentences may have more than one adjective.

1. The sidewalks are icy in the winter.

2. Allison fixed the broken toy for her younger brother.

3. The frightened puppy hid behind the brown couch.

4. Andrew left his bike in the front yard.

5. Mr. James drove his green car to the store.

6. Some smart dogs can be trained to help people.

7. The yogurt tasted sweet.

8. I couldn't carry the heavy bag by myself.

9. There are magnificent sights to see at the national park.

10. The woman wore large earrings.

11. We placed the pumpkins on the wooden bench.

12. Everyone laughed at the funny movie.

Order of Adjectives

- **Adjectives** are words that describe nouns or pronouns.

> Tom bought a **new** painting.

- You can use more than one **adjective** to describe a noun or pronoun.

> Tom bought a **beautiful, new** painting.

- There is an **order of adjectives** that is usually followed when using more than one adjective to describe the same noun or pronoun. The list below shows how the **order of adjectives** is usually presented, but there are some exceptions and different combinations depending on the situation.

Opinion comes before ➡	Size/ Measure comes before ➡	Age comes before ➡	Color comes before ➡	Origin comes before ➡	Material comes before ➡	Purpose
good bad beautiful ugly smart dumb	*size/ measure:* big small high low *shape:* round circular square *condition:* broken cracked ripped fresh rotten	new old young	red purple black green dark light	French German American European Italian Korean	iron brass cotton gold wooden vegetable silk linen	sleeping sailing walking

• You can use the chart on the previous page to put adjectives together to describe a noun or pronoun. When you use more than one adjective to describe a noun or pronoun, you must use commas between the adjectives.

> The **tiny, young, white** puppy slept on the floor.
> We carved faces into the **ugly, big, orange** pumpkins.
> Mom threw away the **broken, green** skateboard.

Now turn to pages 148–149 to practice writing adjectives in the correct order.

6

Name _____

Order of Adjectives

Practice

Read the following sentences and adjectives. Rewrite the sentences using the adjectives. Be sure to write them in the correct order and to use commas.

1. Our town will soon have a (new, big) library.

_____

2. My mom won't let me wear my (Italian, ripped, old) jeans anymore.

_____

3. The (big, magnificent, red) hot-air balloon floated through the sky.

_____

4. Grandpa has a (black, German, noisy) car.

_____

5. The (slow, old) computer needs to be updated.

_____

6. Our soccer team got (new, nice, cotton) jerseys.

_____

Common Core State Standards Literacy Handbook

Name _____

7. Alyssa always wears (gold, small) earrings.

_____

8. We sat on the grass and looked up at the (white, fluffy) clouds.

_____

9. The florist arranged the (fresh, colorful) flowers in the vase.

_____

10. We were nervous about getting on the (small, white) plane.

_____

11. Mark wore a pair of (European, black, leather) shoes.

_____

12. We took the groceries out of the (green, reusable) bags.

_____

Proper and Common Adjectives

- **Proper adjectives** are formed from proper nouns. A proper adjective begins with a capital letter.

> *Michigan winters are cold and long.*

- Some proper adjectives describe languages, races, or nationalities.

> *The store sells Irish jewelry.*

- Brand names are often proper adjectives.
- **Common adjectives** are not formed from proper nouns. Do not capitalize common adjectives.

> *The captain is wearing a blue hat.*

Now turn to page 151 to practice identifying proper and common adjectives.

Name _____

Proper and Common Adjectives

Practice

A. In the following sentences, underline all common adjectives once and all proper adjectives twice.

1. I want to learn how to make delicious Japanese food.

2. Kathryn likes to read stories from Greek mythology.

3. Would you come to my New Year's Eve party?

4. The elderly man has an Australian accent.

5. Our school librarian is an excellent storyteller.

B. Rewrite the sentences below correctly. Remember to capitalize proper adjectives.

6. Look at the Beautiful, african butterfly.

_____

7. My grandmother has an italian accent, and my grandfather has a french accent.

_____

_____

8. We went on a Long tour and learned about spanish architecture.

_____

9. Maria enjoys eating chinese food.

_____

10. I wrote a long essay about my german heritage.

_____

Articles

- An **article** is a type of adjective. These words are articles: *a, an, the.*

> Look at **the** balloons.

- Use *a* and *an* with singular nouns.

> Do you play **an** instrument?
> I took **a** lesson to learn how to play guitar.

- Use *the* before singular and plural nouns.

> **The** grapes grew on **the** vine.

- An **article** comes before the noun it describes. Other words sometimes come between the article and the noun it introduces.

> She opened **the** birthday presents.

Now turn to page 153 to practice using articles in sentences.

Name _____

Articles

Practice

Complete each sentence below by writing an article on the lines provided.

1. My sister really wants _____ dog for her birthday.

2. Did you see _____ big elephants when you were at the zoo?

3. Please hand me _____ bowl of fruit.

4. _____ police officer stopped to ask us questions.

5. We cleaned up _____ broken eggs.

6. Sam drew a picture of _____ igloo.

7. _____ dog barked at me and ran away.

8. Ryan read _____ book about _____ Nile River.

9. We went sailing on _____ lake.

10. I saw _____ Pacific Ocean!

11. Ralph found _____ ant crawling across his book.

12. I need _____ new notebook.

13. We went to the _____ library to do research.

14. _____ road was long and windy.

15. I ordered _____ egg sandwich for lunch.

Adjectives that Compare

- **Adjectives** describe people, places, or things.

  > *Joan stood next to the **tall** building.*

- Add *-er* to most short adjectives to compare two people, places, or things.

  > *My brother is **stronger** than my sister.*

- Add *-est* to most adjectives to compare more than two.

  > *That is the **biggest** lake I have ever seen.*

- For adjectives ending in *e*, drop the *e* before adding *-er* or *-est*.

  > *large–larger–largest*

- For adjectives ending in a consonant and *y*, change the *y* to *i* before adding *-er* or *-est*.

  > *heavy–heavier–heaviest*

- For one-syllable adjectives that have a single vowel before the final consonant, double the final consonant before adding *-er* or *-est*.

  > *red–redder–reddest*

Now turn to pages 155–156 to practice using adjectives that compare.

Name _____

Adjectives that Compare 1

Practice

Think about the comparisons in each sentence. Then rewrite the sentence with the correct form for each underlined adjective.

1. Samoa is probably warm than Canada.

   _____

2. Fire ants are small than a fingernail.

   _____

3. He said that Mr. Andrews was the nice teacher he had ever had.

   _____

4. The distances Lewis and Clark traveled on their Corps of Discovery were long than those of some other expeditions to the West.

   _____

   _____

5. Lewis thought that they were the strange squirrels in the world.

   _____

6. The next day, he saw an even large buffalo.

   _____

7. Two hundred years ago, it was hard to cross the country than it is today.

   _____

8. Birds can change direction fast than a plane.

   _____

Name _____

Adjectives that Compare 2
Practice

Read each sentence. Rewrite it with the correct adjective form.

1. One of the healing plants was leafy than the others.

   _____

2. Even the tiny insects can teach scientists important things about nature.

   _____

3. He felt like the lucky science teacher in the country.

   _____

4. E. O. Wilson worked to make our planet healthy than it was.

   _____

5. Neither Clark nor Lewis was brave than the other.

   _____

6. Lewis and Clark are two of the brave men in history.

   _____

7. Keeping a journal is easy for some people than it is for others.

   _____

8. The men thought it was hot today than it was yesterday.

   _____

Comparing with *More* or *Most*

- **Comparative adjectives** compare two nouns by adding *-er* to an adjective.

  > The audience clapped **louder** today than they did yesterday.

- **Superlative adjectives** compare more than two nouns by adding *-est* to an adjective.

  > That is the **largest** statue I have ever seen.

- For long adjectives, use *more* and *most* to compare people, places, or things.

  > The brown puppy is **more** playful than the white one.
  > The black puppy is the **most** playful puppy.

- Use *more* to compare two people, places, or things.

  > This tree has **more** orange leaves than that one.

- Use *most* to compare more than two.

  > California is the **most** beautiful place I have ever seen.

- When you use *more* and *most*, do not use the ending *-er* or *-est*. Never add *-er* and *more* to the same adjective. Never add *-est* and *most* to the same adjective.

- For some common two-syllable adjectives, such as *happy* and *healthy*, use the ending *-er* or *-est* instead.

  > She is **happier** than she was yesterday.
  > She is the **happiest** she has ever been.

Now turn to pages 158–160 to practice comparing with *more* or *most*.

Name _____

Comparing with *More* or *Most* 1

Practice

Rewrite the sentences. Correct any adjectives that are used incorrectly.

1. John tried to find the nicer place of all to stay.

   _____

2. He thought the Navajo language made the great code.

   _____

3. Grandfather's home was prettiest than the school.

   _____

4. Hiking was hard than hauling water.

   _____

5. The Navajo language was the United States' stronger weapon.

   _____

6. Some soldiers were fastest than others.

   _____

7. This code was simplest than any other.

   _____

8. This is the stranger story of all.

   _____

Name _____

Comparing with *More* or *Most* 2

Practice

Read the sentences. If the sentence is correct, write correct on the line. If it is not correct, rewrite the sentence using the correct form of the adjective.

1. Most importantest was that the Navajo language had no alphabet.

   _____

   _____

2. This story is the most interestingest that I have ever read.

   _____

   _____

3. Everyone tries to contribute his or her most sincere efforts in wartime.

   _____

   _____

4. The most dangerousest time was the day that the enemy shot at Grandfather.

   _____

   _____

5. It was more fascinatinger to watch the stars than to go to school.

   _____

   _____

Name _____

6. John wanted to learn to write more difficult codes.

_____

_____

7. The Navajo language was considered more secreter than other languages.

_____

_____

8. A wild horse feels more comfortabler without a rope around its neck.

_____

_____

Comparing with *Good*

- In comparisons, the adjective *good* has an irregular form. *Better* and *best* are the irregular forms of *good*.

> I thought the book was **good.**
>
> I thought the movie was **better** than the book.
>
> I thought the play was the **best.**

- Use *better* to compare two people, places, or things.

> I got a **better** grade on this test than the last one.

- Use *best* to compare more than two people, places, or things.

> This was the **best** birthday party I've been to!

Now turn to pages 162–163 to practice comparing with *good.*

6

Name _____

Comparing with *Good*

Practice

Read each sentence. If the form of the adjective is correct, write correct on the line. If it is wrong, circle it and write the correct form.

1. Ana Rosa imagines that being a writer would be the better job in the world.

   _____

2. Mami makes better *dulces* than *batatas fritas*.

   _____

3. Many tourists think that Sosúa Bay is the bestest part of the República Dominicana.

   _____

4. Some people thought that one plan was best than the other.

   _____

5. Mami thought that Ana Rosa's story was the best story that she had ever heard.

   _____

6. Seeing a whale is even gooder than seeing a sea monster.

   _____

7. The sea monster went to the bestest underwater fiesta in the ocean.

   _____

Name _____

8. Writing a story was better than putting up a billboard.

_____

9. Mami is the goodest cook in town.

_____

10. Ana Rosa thinks her gri gri tree is the better spot for looking around.

_____

Comparing with *Bad*

- In comparisons, the adjective *bad* has an irregular form. *Worse* and *worst* are the irregular forms of *bad*.

> That was a **bad** song.
>
> This song is **worse** than the other one.
>
> That was the **worst** song I have ever heard.

- Use *worse* to compare two people, places, or things.

> The puppy behaved **worse** than the kitten.

- Use *worst* to compare more than two people, places, or things.

> That was the **worst** sandwich I have ever eaten.

Now turn to pages 165–166 to practice comparing with *bad*.

Name _____

Comparing with *Bad*

Practice

Rewrite each sentence, correcting the form of *bad* where necessary.

1. Winter is the worse time to visit the República Dominicana.

   _____

   _____

2. Making a fuss about the sea monster would be worst than not telling anybody.

   _____

   _____

3. Guario thinks that sitting in a gri gri tree is the worser way to spend time.

   _____

   _____

4. Roberto complained that washing dishes was a worst chore than sweeping.

   _____

   _____

5. Spring is a worst time than winter for whales to migrate.

   _____

   _____

Name _____

6. Spotting the sea monster was not the worse thing that happened that day.

_____

_____

7. Roberto was a worser domino player than Papi.

_____

_____

8. Ana Rosa had a worst time at the gathering than her neighbors.

_____

_____

Lesson F
Adverbs

We use adverbs to tell more about verbs. Adverbs help us describe how, when, where, or why an action takes place. We also use adverbs to compare people, places, and things.

Adverbs

- An **adverb** is a word that tells *more* about a verb, an adjective, or another adverb.

  > Rick **quietly** walked into the room.

- Some **adverbs** tell *how* an action takes place. These adverbs may describe how completely an action is performed.

  > Renee **quickly** ran away.
  >
  > She **completely** ignored the people around her.

- Some **adverbs** tell *when* an action takes place. These adverbs may describe how often an action takes place.

  > Will **recently** started playing the piano.
  >
  > He practices piano **daily.**

- Some **adverbs** tell *where* an action takes place.

  > Madeline doesn't like going **there**.

Now turn to pages 168–169 to practice identifying and writing adverbs.

6

Name _____

Adverbs 1
Practice

Underline the adverb in each sentence. On the line, write whether the adverb describes how, when, or where.

1. Alexi walked slowly through the woods. _____

2. The Golden Mare left early to reach the Lake of the Sun. _____

3. Angry at the Tsar's words, Alexi trembled inside. _____

4. The Golden Mare galloped rapidly through the forest. _____

5. The Firebird cried softly in its cage. _____

6. He hunted late into the night. _____

7. The Tsar treated the Firebird cruelly. _____

8. The Firebird flew high into the sky. _____

9. Alexi and Yelena the Fair were happily married. _____

10. Alexi and the Golden Mare always remained friends. _____

Name _____

Adverbs 2

Practice

A. In these sentences, the adverbs describe verbs, adverbs, or adjectives. Underline each adverb. Some sentences contain more than one adverb.

1. The Golden Mare spoke quietly.

2. Yelena the Fair realized that she would be in danger very soon.

3. The Tsar was terribly angry about Alexi's success.

4. The Lake of the Sun shone brilliantly in the morning.

5. The Water of Youth began to boil very quickly.

B. Complete each sentence with an adverb that describes the underlined word. Choose from the adverbs in the box.

almost	very	completely	finally	quite	rather	too

6. The Tsar acted _____ greedily.

7. They poured water into the iron pot until it was _____ full.

8. The ship moved _____ gracefully across the water.

9. Alexi stayed awake _____ late that night.

10. Alexi and the Golden Mare _____ defeated the Tsar.

Using *Good* and *Well*

- *Good* is an adjective and is used to describe nouns.

> Leah did a **good** job on her book report.

- *Well* is an adverb that tells *how* about a verb.

> The performer dances **well.**

- Do not confuse the adjective *good* with the adverb *well*.

> Our city has a **good** football team.
> Our city's football team played **well.**

- Use *well* as an adjective when you refer to someone's health.

> Dan wasn't feeling **well,** so he stayed home from school.

Now turn to page 171 to practice using *good* and *well*.

Name _____

Using *Good* and *Well*

Practice

A. Read both sentences in each pair. Circle the letter of the sentence that uses *good* or *well* correctly.

1. a. The Golden Mare was a good friend to Alexi.

   b. The Golden Mare was a well friend to Alexi.

2. a. Yelena the Fair hid her plan good.

   b. Yelena the Fair hid her plan well.

3. a. Alexi ruled good.

   b. Alexi ruled well.

4. a. They played a good trick on the Tsar.

   b. They played a well trick on the Tsar.

5. a. The Tsar did not treat Alexi well.

   b. The Tsar did not treat Alexi good.

B. Write *well* or *good* to complete each sentence correctly. Then underline the word that *good* or *well* describes.

6. Alexi was a _____ ruler to his people.

7. The Tsar thought that if he planned _____ he could wed Yelena the Fair.

8. The Tsar would not be a _____ husband.

9. Alexi and the Golden Mare worked _____ together.

10. The Golden Mare promised to serve Alexi _____.

Comparing with Adverbs: *-er* and *-est*

- An **adverb** can compare two or more actions.

> *Jeff swam **faster** than Vanessa did.*

- Add *-er* to most short adverbs to compare two actions.

> *Vickie climbed **higher** than Tim did.*

- Add *-est* to most short adverbs to compare more than two actions.

> *Todd climbed the **highest** of all.*

Now turn to page 173 to practice comparing with adverbs.

Name _____

Comparing with Adverbs: *-er* and *-est*

Practice

Read the sentences. Write the correct form of the adverb in parentheses.

1. (hard) Teddy pounded the tent stakes _____ than Bobby did.

2. (near) Of the three, Teddy was the one standing _____ to the raccoon.

3. (fast) It was Teddy who ran _____ of all.

4. (soon) Bobby wished that he had spoken up _____ than he did.

5. (high) The mountain rose _____ than any of San Francisco's skyscrapers.

6. (hard) Of the three of them, Uncle Curtis laughed _____.

7. (fast) Teddy walked _____ than Bobby and Uncle Curtis.

8. (soon) The raccoon arrived _____ of all.

9. (late) They arrived at the campsite _____ than Uncle Curtis expected.

10. (fast) The other campers pitched their tents _____ than Uncle Curtis did.

Comparing with Adverbs: Using *More* and *Most*

- Use *more* or *most* to form comparisons with adverbs that end in *-ly* and with most other adverbs that have two or more syllables.

> Maggie performed **more** confidently after she practiced.
>
> She practices the **most** frequently of all the performers.

- Use *more* to compare two actions, and use *most* to compare more than two actions.

> Veronica moved **more** quickly than her brother did.
>
> Those flowers were the **most** beautifully arranged creations I've ever seen.

- When you use *more* or *most*, do not use the ending *-er* or *-est*.

> Grandpa drove **more** slowly after his accident.
>
> Uncle Bart drives the **most** slowly of everyone in the family.

Now turn to pages 175–176 to practice comparing with adverbs using *more* and *most*.

Name _____

Comparing with Adverbs: Using *More* and *Most* 1

Practice

A. Read the sentences. Write the correct form of the adverb in parentheses using *more* or *most*.

1. (hungrily) Of them all, it was Teddy who stared at the hot dogs _____.

2. (patiently) Bobby waited _____ than Teddy did.

3. (quietly) Bobby worked _____ of them all.

4. (quickly) Teddy walked _____ than Bobby did.

5. (easily) Uncle Curtis got lost _____ than Teddy did.

B. Read each sentence. If the adverb is correct, write Correct on the line. If it is not Correct, rewrite the sentence with the correct form of the adverb.

6. Uncle Curtis grinned happiliest of all.

   _____

7. Bobby learned more quicklier than Teddy.

   _____

8. Uncle Curtis ate slowlier than the boys.

   _____

9. Teddy treated the map more carefully than did Uncle Curtis.

   _____

10. Teddy eats more noisily of all.

   _____

Name _____

Comparing with Adverbs: Using *More* and *Most* 2

Practice

Read each sentence. If the sentence uses more or most correctly, write Correct. Otherwise, rewrite the sentence correctly.

1. The ranger spoke most knowledgeably than Uncle Curtis did.

   _____

2. Teddy unpacked the car more hurriedlier than Bobby did.

   _____

3. Uncle Curtis turned more promptlier the third time they neared the exit.

   _____

4. Of the three of them, it was Teddy who looked at the raccoon most angrily.

   _____

5. The experienced campers found the trail more easilier than Uncle Curtis did.

   _____

   _____

6. Bobby asked questions most eagerly than Teddy did.

   _____

7. It was Teddy who unrolled his sleeping bag most roughliest of all.

   _____

8. The raccoon found the marshmallows more quickly than did Teddy.

   _____

   _____

Avoiding Double Negatives

- A **negative** is a word that means "no," such as *not*, *never*, *nobody*, *nowhere*, and the contraction *n't*.

> I have **never** traveled to Europe.
>
> Mark **hasn't** traveled to Europe either.

- Do not use two negatives in the same sentence. When you use two negatives in the same sentence it is called a double negative, and the sentence must be fixed.

- You can fix a sentence with two negatives by removing one of the negatives or by changing one negative word to a positive word.

Negative	Positive
no, none	any
never	ever
nothing	anything
nobody	anybody
no one	anyone
nowhere	anywhere

Incorrect Sentence: *Ann **didn't** think **nothing** about her science project.*
Correct Sentence: *Ann **didn't** think about her science project.*

Incorrect Sentence: *The pilot **could not** find **nowhere** to land.*
Correct Sentence: *The pilot **could not** find **anywhere** to land.*

Now turn to pages 178–180 to practice avoiding double negatives.

6

Name _____

Avoiding Double Negatives 1
Practice

Correct the sentences by removing one of the negatives. Write your answers on the lines.

1. Some children never not exercise.

_____

2. Until now, nobody never learned how to sail.

_____

3. Yesterday she couldn't give no directions to the taxi driver.

_____

4. Athletes don't never give up.

_____

5. Hannah couldn't play on no playgrounds.

_____

6. Nothing nowhere was written in Braille.

_____

Name _____

7. The girl had never played with no other kids.

_____

8. Matthew never had no fun on the swings.

_____

9. Jennifer never forgets no kind words.

_____

10. She can't not stop trying.

_____

Name _____

Avoiding Double Negatives 2
Practice

Rewrite each sentence, replacing one of the negative words with a positive word.

1. The kids never have nothing bad to say about gym class.

_____

_____

2. No one never passes up a chance to learn kick boxing.

_____

_____

3. No person nowhere should be without a new GPS device.

_____

_____

4. What if you couldn't find nobody to give you directions?

_____

_____

5. None of the athletes say nothing negative.

_____

_____

6. There weren't no playgrounds where she could play.

_____

_____

Common Core State Standards Literacy Handbook

Relative Adverbs

- An **adverb** tells more about a verb. It can tell *how, when, where,* or *why* an action takes place.

> Margaret **immediately** called her parents.

- A **relative adverb** introduces a clause that tells more about a noun. A clause is a group of words that includes a subject and a predicate. Relative adverbs can be used instead of a relative pronoun plus a preposition. There are three main **relative adverbs**: *where, when,* and *why.*

> This is the restaurant **in which** we ate dinner. (relative pronoun plus preposition)
> This is the restaurant **where** we ate dinner. (relative adverb)

- The relative adverb *where* means "in which" or "at which" and is used to refer to a place.

> Here is the place **where** we will meet if there is an emergency.

- The relative adverb *when* means "in which" or "at which" and is used to refer to a time expression.

> Monday is the day **when** we will practice the fire drill.

- The relative adverb *why* means "for which" and is used to refer to a reason.

> Do you know the reason **why** some animals hibernate in the winter?

Now turn to page 182 to practice using relative adverbs.

Name _____

Relative Adverbs

Practice

Read the sentences below. Fill in the blanks with the correct relative adverb.

1. November is the month _____ we celebrate Thanksgiving Day.

2. Today we learned the reason _____ the seasons change.

3. I always look forward to the day _____ we begin our summer vacation.

4. My parents visited the place _____ they first met.

5. Sally doesn't know the reason _____ Elizabeth won't talk to her.

6. I like vacationing at places _____ there are outdoor activities.

7. Do you know the time _____ we are supposed to meet?

8. The firefighter asked if we knew the place _____ the fire started.

9. Holidays are a time _____ people celebrate.

10. There must be a reason _____ you don't want to go the movie.

Lesson G
Prepositions, Conjunctions, and Interjections

When we speak and write we use prepositions to relate a noun or pronoun to another word in a sentence. We use conjunctions to join parts of a sentence, and we use interjections to show emotion. Prepositions, conjunctions, and interjections are important parts of grammar.

Prepositions

- A **preposition** comes before a noun or pronoun and relates that noun or pronoun to another word in the sentence.

> Marianne walked **down** the stairs.

- Common prepositions are *about, above, across, after, around, at, before, behind, by, down, during, for, from, in, into, near, of, on, over, to, under,* and *with.*

> The plane flew **above** the clouds.
> Harry talked to the woman **behind** the counter.

Now turn to page 184 to practice identifying prepositions.

6

Name _____

Prepositions

Practice

Read each sentence. Underline the prepositions. There may be more than one preposition in each sentence.

1. The balloon flew above the village.

2. Jean-Pierre Blanchard floated over the English Channel.

3. A duck, a rooster, and a sheep rode in the basket of the balloon.

4. The balloon rose to a height of one hundred feet.

5. They floated in a new direction.

6. Weather balloons give us information about the atmosphere.

7. Buoyancy keeps balloons in the air.

8. Bertrand Piccard stayed in a balloon for 20 days.

9. The balloon dropped gently from the sky.

10. The balloon landed in a forest behind a field.

Prepositional Phrases

- A **prepositional phrase** is a group of words that begins with a **preposition** and ends with a noun or pronoun.

> The children ran **around the park.**

- A **prepositional phrase** makes a connection between two nouns or pronouns in a sentence.

> <u>Heather</u> walked **over** the <u>bridge</u>.

- The **object of a preposition** is the noun or pronoun that follows the preposition. When a pronoun follows a preposition, it should be an object pronoun, such as *me, you, him, her, it, us,* or *them.*

> Josh stood near the **counter.**
> Laurie stood behind **me.**

Now turn to page 186 to practice using prepositional phrases.

6

Name _____

Prepositional Phrases

Practice

A. Underline the preposition in each sentence. Circle the object of the preposition.

1. Jacques Charles learned about hydrogen.

2. They waved from the balloon.

3. Balloonists cannot be afraid of heights.

4. François Pilâtre De Rozier anchored his balloon with a tether.

5. The first human passenger flew over Paris.

B. Complete each prepositional phrase by writing a preposition on the line.

6. The wind was strong _____ the day that they left.

7. There were 25 members _____ the balloon club.

8. A duck, a rooster, and a sheep rode _____ the balloon.

9. _____ the field, the balloonists prepared to launch.

10. The balloons _____ the sky were a beautiful sight.

Coordinating Conjunctions

- A **coordinating conjunction** joins parts of a sentence that are grammatically equal or similar. A coordinating conjunction shows that the parts it joins are similar in importance and structure.

> *The girls ate a sandwich **and** pretzels for lunch.*
>
> *Maria likes turkey sandwiches, **but** Andrew likes ham sandwiches.*

- **Coordinating conjunctions** always come **between** the words or clauses that they join.

> *Should I wear the blue tennis shoes **or** the red tennis shoes?*

- A **coordinating conjunction** can join a word to a word.

> *We bought lemons **and** limes at the store.*

- A **coordinating conjunction** can join a phrase to a phrase.

> *We can jog through the park **or** on the track.*

- A **coordinating conjunction** can join a clause to a clause.

> *What you do **and** what you say are important things to think about.*

- A **coordinating conjunction** can join three or more words, phrases, or clauses to create a series. When this happens, use commas between the elements.

> *We decorated the room with balloons, streamers, and confetti.*

6

- When a coordinating conjunction joins independent clauses, place a comma before the conjunction.

> *Stacey wants to be an actress someday, **so** she is taking theater classes.*

- There are seven **coordinating conjunctions:** *and, or, for, nor, but, yet, so.*

Now turn to page 189 to practice using coordinating conjunctions.

Name _____

Coordinating Conjunctions

Practice

Complete each sentence by writing a coordinating conjunction on the line provided.

1. Mark wants to play on the basketball team, _____ he has a broken leg.

2. Would you rather play soccer _____ football?

3. Liza spent her weekend studying for her math, writing, _____ reading classes.

4. Sarah plays golf, _____ her favorite sport is tennis.

5. I was tired, _____ I took a nap.

6. Is this seat taken, _____ may I sit here?

7. Amelia gets nervous in large gatherings, _____ it is no surprise that she avoids crowded places.

8. The chicken soup is hot _____ delicious.

9. My cat loves having his head scratched, _____ he hates getting his claws trimmed.

10. Sue ignored my phone calls, _____ I sent her an e-mail.

Subordinating Conjunctions

- A **subordinate (or dependent) clause** is a group of words that *cannot* stand alone—it depends on the rest of the sentence for its meaning. A clause always has a subject and a predicate. Subordinate clauses often begin with a conjunction, such as *after, because, when, if, since, though,* or *where.*

> *after they left*

- A **main clause** is a group of words that *can* stand alone.

> *We went to the park.*

- A **subordinating conjunction** joins a dependent clause with a main clause.

> *We went to the park after they left.*

- Some **subordinating conjunctions** include *after, although, as long as, before, because, if, since, unless, until, wherever, while,* and *once.*

> ***Although*** *I want to go to your party, I'm too sick to attend.*
> ***Because*** *she wanted to be a teacher, she studied hard in school.*
> *You can go swimming **as long as** an adult is present.*

Now turn to page 191 to practice using subordinating conjunctions.

Name _____

Subordinating Conjunctions

Practice

Read the sentences below. Then circle the subordinating conjunction in each sentence.

1. Although I enjoy movies, I don't want to see this one.

2. Because it was late, we went home after the movie.

3. After I finished my math test, I walked to the cafeteria for lunch.

4. Whenever I feel homesick, I look at pictures of my family.

5. Once you arrive, check in with the front desk.

6. Veronica doesn't want to go swimming because the water is cold.

7. I'm not allowed to have a cell phone until I'm older.

8. Although I like orange juice, I don't like oranges.

9. You shouldn't try to write a book report until you've finished reading the book.

10. Don't volunteer to help unless you have the time to spare.

Correlative Conjunctions

Some conjunctions combine with other words to form **correlative conjunctions.** Correlative conjunctions are always used in pairs. They join similar elements in a sentence. Below is a list of the most common correlative conjunctions.

---

either—or

neither—nor

not only—but also

whether—or

both—and

Either you **or** Steve should go to the store.

Neither Paul **nor** Patty has passed the test.

She **not only** wrote the screenplay for the movie **but also** directed it.

Whether we meet at the park **or** at your house is up to you.

Both my mother **and** my father were smiling.

Now turn to pages 193–195 to practice using correlative conjunctions.

Name _____

Correlative Conjunctions 1
Practice

Paying attention to the expressions used in the following sentences, fill in the blanks with the words *or*, *nor*, *but also*, or *and*.

1. I have both respect _____ admiration for them.

2. It will rain either today _____ tomorrow.

3. He is neither mad _____ upset.

4. I do not know whether he has seen the movie before _____ not.

5. We not only dressed up for the holiday _____ decorated the school.

6. The crowd was both large _____ excited.

7. We should either walk quickly _____ take the bus.

8. I don't know whether I want to study Spanish _____ Russian.

9. Both my uncle _____ my cousin live in New York.

10. Neither my brother _____ my sister can go to the game.

Name _____

Correlative Conjunctions 2

Practice

Read the sentences below. Then circle the correlative conjunctions that complete each sentence.

1. _____ Alex _____ Carlos tried out for the school play.

   a. Whether . . . or

   b. Both . . . and

2. _____ you clean your room _____ you will stay home this weekend.

   a. Either . . . or

   b. Neither . . . nor

3. _____ we go home _____ stay at the park doesn't matter to me.

   a. Whether . . . or

   b. Not only . . . but also

4. _____ _____ did she do well on her math test, _____ she

   _____ got an A on her social studies report.

   a. Both . . . and

   b. Not only . . . but also

5. _____ I can go to the movies on Saturday, _____ I can go to the mall.

   a. Not only . . . but also

   b. Either . . . or

Name _____

6. I found _____ my homework _____ my textbook on the kitchen counter.

   a. both . . . and

   b. either . . . or

7. Paula found _____ _____ the shoes she had lost _____

_____ her favorite jacket.

   a. neither . . . nor

   b. not only . . . but also

8. I have _____ the time _____ the motivation to play basketball right now.

   a. neither . . . nor

   b. either . . . or

9. _____ my stereo _____ my television stopped working last night.

   a. Both . . . and

   b. Whether . . . or

10. I can't decide _____ to play soccer this year _____ to take dance lessons.

   a. neither . . . nor

   b. whether . . . or

Interjections

- An **interjection** is a word or a phrase that shows excitement or emotion.

- Use a comma to separate interjections from the rest of the sentence.

> **Yes,** I want to go to the zoo today!

- If the interjection shows a very strong emotion, use an exclamation point.

> **Oh wow!** I forgot to turn in my homework.

Now turn to page 197 to practice using interjections.

Name _____

Interjections

Practice

A. Circle the interjections in the sentences below.

1. Oh no! Did you hurt yourself?

2. Hey! What a great idea!

3. Oh! I've got a toothache.

4. Ouch! That hurts!

5. Oh, please say you'll come to my party.

6. Yes, I'll come to your party.

B. Rewrite the sentences using correct capitalization and adding commas or exclamation points after the interjections.

7. Wow that is wonderful

   _____

8. Yikes we forgot to replace the batteries

   _____

9. Oh did you know that this Friday is a holiday

   _____

10. Hooray we will have pictures to remember our trip

    _____

11. Look there is a pencil in my backpack

    _____

Standard
2

Lesson H
Capitalization

Capitalization is an important part of writing. Capitalization helps readers and speakers know when a new sentence has started, when the name of a person or place is being referred to, what the title of a book is, and much more.

First Words

• Capitalize the first word of a sentence.

> *My sister is going to camp.*

• Capitalize the first word of a direct quotation. Do not capitalize the second part of an interrupted quotation.

> *Dan cried, "Please stop the presses!"*
> *"I am leaving," Jan declared, "as soon as I can."*

• When the second part of a quotation is a new sentence, put a period after the interrupting expression and capitalize the first word of the new sentence.

> *"I know that song," said Lisa. "We learned it last week."*

• Capitalize all words in the greeting of a letter.

> *Dear Sirs:*   *Dear Friend,*

• Capitalize the first word in the closing of a letter.

> *Sincerely,*   *Yours truly,*

- Capitalize the first word of each line of poetry, unless the word is not capitalized in the original piece.

> *I shot an arrow into the air,*
> *It fell to earth, I know not where;*
> *For, so swiftly it flew, the sight*
> *Could not follow in its flight.*

Now turn to page 200 to practice capitalizing first words.

Name _____

First Words

Practice

Rewrite the friendly letter correctly. Use capital letters where needed.

(1) dear georgia,

(2) how are you? Let me just say,

(3) "here is a poem for you."

(4) roses are red.
Violets are blue.
Sugar is sweet
and so are you.

(5) your friend,
Michael

_____

_____

_____

_____

_____

_____

_____

_____

Proper Nouns: Names and Titles of People

- **Capitalize** the names of people and the initials that stand for their names.

> James Robert Perry   J. R. Perry

- Capitalize the titles or abbreviations of titles when they come before or after the names of people.

> Mr. James Perry, Jr.   General J. P. Perry
>
> Dr. Ellen Mahoney

- Capitalize words that show family relationships when used as titles or as substitutes for a person's name.

> Then Dad and Grandma Ellen cooked dinner.

- Do not capitalize words that show family relationships when they are preceded by a possessive noun or pronoun.

> Diane's grandmother is a good cook. Her dad is a good cook too.

- Capitalize the pronoun *I*.

> Can I help cook dinner?

Now turn to pages 202–203 to practice capitalizing the names and titles of people.

Name _____

Proper Nouns: Names and Titles of People

Practice

Rewrite each sentence correctly. Capitalize the names and titles of people where needed.

1. p. j. and I made brownies for the family party.

   _____

   _____

2. My uncle, general steven ross, loved them.

   _____

   _____

3. My uncle and i ate five brownies each.

   _____

   _____

4. Father helped grandpa make pasta.

   _____

   _____

5. Grandpa said that mr. matthews gave him the recipe.

   _____

   _____

Name _____

6. grandma ruth said that my little sister, peggy, can help make brownies next year.

_____

_____

7. peggy and i are very excited that we'll get to make brownies together soon!

_____

_____

8. Our neighbor mrs. pirrello told us that she has a good cookie recipe.

_____

_____

9. My mom and my Dad want to try Mrs. pirrello's cookie recipe.

_____

_____

10. p. j. and my Sister ate almost all of the brownies we made!

_____

_____

Proper Nouns: Names of Places

- **Capitalize** the names of cities, states, countries, and continents. Do not capitalize articles or prepositions that are part of the name.

> City—Austin
> State—Texas
> Country—the United States of America
> Continent—North America

- Capitalize the names of bodies of water and geographical features.

> Atlantic Ocean   Niagara Falls

- Capitalize the names of sections of the country.

> the South   the Pacific Northwest

- Do not capitalize compass points when they just show direction.

> New York is east of Cleveland.

- Capitalize the names of streets and highways.

> Elm Street   Santa Ana Freeway

- Capitalize the names of buildings, bridges, and monuments.

> Willis Tower   Brooklyn Bridge
> Jefferson Memorial

- Capitalize the names of stars and planets.

> The closest star to our planet is Proxima Centauri.
>
> The planet closest to the sun is Mercury.

- Capitalize *Earth* when it refers to the planet. Do not capitalize *earth* when preceded by *the*. Do not capitalize *sun* or *moon*.

> One moon revolves around Earth.
>
> The earth revolves around the sun.

Now turn to page 206 to practice capitalizing the names of places.

6

Name _____

Proper Nouns: Names of Places

Practice

Rewrite each sentence correctly. Use capital letters where needed.

1. Our class drove through titusville, florida, to visit the john f. kennedy space center.

   _____

   _____

2. The bus drove south along cheney highway.

   _____

   _____

3. We looked at the atlantic ocean, and then we went inside to learn about space.

   _____

   _____

4. We learned about the crab nebula, an exploding star far from earth.

   _____

   _____

5. We also learned about mars, the fourth planet from the sun.

   _____

   _____

Other Proper Nouns and Adjectives

- Capitalize the names of schools, clubs, businesses, and political parties.

> *Albright Middle School*   *Explorers' Club*
>
> *Reynold's Pharmacy*   *Democratic Party*

- Capitalize the names of historic events, periods of time, and documents.

> *Battle of Bunker Hill*   *Colonial Period*
>
> *Declaration of Independence*

- Capitalize the days of the week, months of the year, and holidays. Do not capitalize the names of the seasons.

> *We started school on Tuesday, September 1.*
>
> *Our first vacation is on Labor Day.*
>
> *My favorite season is autumn.*

- Capitalize abbreviations.

> *Dr.*   *Ave.*   *Sept.*   *Ln.*

- Capitalize the names of ethnic groups, nationalities, and languages.

> *The French won the war.*
>
> *I speak Japanese.*

- Capitalize proper adjectives that are formed from the names of ethnic groups and nationalities.

> *Italian bread*   *Egyptian cotton*

6

• Capitalize the first word of each main topic and subtopic in an outline.

I. Products and exports
    A. Natural resources
    B. Manufactured goods

Now turn to page 209 to practice capitalizing other proper nouns and adjectives.

Name _____

Other Proper Nouns and Adjectives

Practice

Rewrite each sentence correctly. Use capital letters where needed.

1. The fifth graders at jefferson elementary are studying the louisiana purchase.

   _____

   _____

2. The jeffersonville historical society has helped them gather information.

   _____

   _____

3. The Louisiana Territory had been changing hands since the seven years' war.

   _____

   _____

4. spanish, french, and british troops had all occupied the territory.

   _____

   _____

5. The students wondered if the troops spoke english.

   _____

   _____

Titles of Works

Capitalize the first, last, and all important words in the title of a book, play, short story, poem, film, article, newspaper, magazine, TV series, chapter of a book, and song.

> I can't wait to read *Roll of Thunder, Hear My Cry.*
>
> Did you see *Peter Pan* at the community theater?
>
> A clever short story is "Rip Van Winkle."
>
> My favorite poem when I was young was "Old King Cole."
>
> You should read "Cars of the Future" in this month's *Vehicles Monthly.*
>
> My dad reads the *Los Angeles Times* every morning.
>
> Did you watch *Newsbreaker* last night?
>
> Chapter one of that book is titled "The Long Night."
>
> I sang "The Star-Spangled Banner" before the big game.

Now turn to pages 211–212 to practice capitalizing the titles of works.

Name _____

Titles of Works

Practice

Rewrite each sentence correctly. Capitalize all titles of works.

1. Our school newspaper, *the titan times*, prints entertainment reviews.

_____

_____

2. One writer liked the book *stuart little*.

_____

_____

3. Her favorite chapter was titled "a narrow escape."

_____

_____

4. Another writer reviewed a play titled *the great divide*.

_____

_____

5. He compared it to the short story titled "opposite ends."

_____

_____

6. One writer reviewed the choir's performance of "somewhere over the rainbow."

_____

_____

Part 6
LANGUAGE:
6.1 Conventions of Standard English

Name _____

7. I remember that song from the film *the wizard of oz*.

_____

_____

8. Next month, I'll write a review for the television series titled *karate man*.

_____

_____

9. The article's title will be "getting your kicks."

_____

_____

10. Maybe I'll write a review of my favorite magazine, *kidsports*.

_____

_____

Lesson I
Punctuation

Punctuation helps readers and speakers know when to pause, when a question is being asked, when a sentence has ended, and much more. There are many different types of punctuation, all of which are used at different times.

End Punctuation

- Use end punctuation at the end of a sentence.

- A **period** (.) ends a declarative sentence. A **declarative sentence** makes a statement.

> *I have a cold.*

- A **period** (.) ends an imperative sentence. An **imperative sentence** makes a command or a request.

> *Keep yourself warm.*

- A **question mark** (?) ends an interrogative sentence. An **interrogative sentence** asks a question.

> *Will I get well?*

- An **exclamation point** (!) ends an exclamatory sentence. An **exclamatory sentence** expresses strong emotion.

> *I finally feel better!*

- An **exclamation point** can also end an imperative sentence.

> *Don't touch that hot burner!*

- Use a period at the end of an abbreviation (in informal writing).

> *Dr.   St.   Tues.   Jan.*

- Use a period in abbreviations for time (in both formal and informal writing).

> *12:00 A.M.   12:00 P.M.*

- Use a period after initials.

> *P. J. Reynolds*

- Use a period after numbers and letters in an outline.

> *I. Margaret Mead*
>   *A. Famous anthropologist*
>   *B. Summary of her work*

Now turn to page 215 to practice end punctuation.

Name _____

End Punctuation

Practice

Write each sentence. Use correct punctuation.

1. Do you have any chicken soup

_____

2. At 10:00 AM, some ladies brought chicken soup to my house.

_____

3. I liked Mrs Nelson's chicken soup best.

_____

4. "AJ Jones," she said, "you'll feel better soon"

_____

5. How hot it was

_____

6. "Do you have more soup?" I asked

_____

Commas

- Use a **comma** (**,**) between the name of the city and state in an address.

  Boston, Massachusetts

- Use a comma after the name of a state or a country when it is used with the name of a city in a sentence.

  We visited San Francisco, California, on our vacation.

- Use a comma between the day and year in a date.

  April 20, 2002   July 4, 1776

- Use a comma before and after the year when it is used with both the month and the day in a sentence. Do not use a comma if only the month and the year are given.

  June 4, 2000, is our last day of school.
  We will begin middle school in September 2001.

- Use a comma after the greeting in a friendly letter and after the closing in all letters.

  Dear Tyler,   Sincerely,

- Use commas to separate three or more items in a series.

  Our flag is red, white, and blue.
  You are kind, patient, and helpful.

- Use a comma before *and*, *but*, or *or* when it joins simple sentences to form a compound sentence.

> We like to play softball, but the field is often muddy.
>
> My mother can drive us, or we can take the bus.

- Use a comma to set off a noun of direct address.

> Greta, please pass the mustard.
>
> Is that you, Mark?

- Use a comma to set off the words *yes* and *no* when they appear at the beginning of a sentence.

> Yes, I would like to join you for a walk.
>
> No, I can't come over after school.

- Use a comma to separate an introductory element, such as a word or a phrase, from the rest of the sentence.

> Well, I didn't mean to get upset.
>
> To get a seat, you'd better come early.
>
> First, boil a cup of water.

- Use a comma after an introductory prepositional phrase.

> To the right of the tree, you'll see the monument.
>
> Behind the house, my family is waiting.

6

- Use a comma to set off a tag question from the rest of the sentence.

> *You want to join us, don't you?*
>
> *It's true that you don't want to go swimming, isn't it?*

- Use a comma to set off a direct quotation.

> *"I'll be right there," I said.*
>
> *"Will you please," I added, "pass the salt?"*

- Use a comma to prevent misreading.

> *To a tall girl like Joan, Taylor seems really short.*

Now turn to pages 219–222 to practice using commas.

Name _____

Commas 1

Practice

A. Rewrite the following friendly letter. Place commas where needed.

124 Higgins Street
(1) Pittsburgh PA 15212
(2) September 4 2009

(3) Dear Mariela

(4) On September 30 2009 I will be coming to town. I can't wait to see you!

(5) Your friend
Grace

_____

_____

_____

_____

_____

_____

_____

_____

B. Rewrite each sentence correctly. Add commas where they are needed.

1. We unloaded the balls bats and catcher's equipment for the big game.

_____

2. I hope I'll be pitcher but I'm not sure whether I'll be chosen.

_____

Name _____

3. A pitcher has to be smart fast and accurate.

_____

4. Our games are exciting and many people cheer.

_____

5. We score early in the game or we depend on good pitching.

_____

6. Yes we can leave when the game is over.

_____

7. You had a good time didn't you?

_____

8. It was so nice to see you Lori.

_____

9. After class ended I went to my locker to gather my books.

_____

10. Graham I can't hear what you're saying.

_____

Name _____

Commas 2

Practice

Rewrite each sentence. Add commas where needed.

1. Mom are you ready for the family reunion?

_____

2. Yes I'm ready.

_____

3. Well I'm not.

_____

4. As you know we haven't prepared anything for the potluck supper.

_____

5. On the table you'll find the recipe for the beans.

_____

Name _____

6. In the cabinet over the stove you'll find the ingredients.

_____

7. Yes Mom I'll make the beans.

_____

8. Like my mom I enjoy cooking.

_____

9. "You are both great cooks" my dad said.

_____

10. "I think" I replied "you're right!"

_____

Semicolons

- Use a **semicolon** (;) to separate two independent clauses (or complete sentences) that are closely related in meaning.

> *I had a great weekend; I visited with friends, played soccer, and ate a good meal.*

- The words *however, moreover, thus,* and *therefore* can be used with a semicolon to separate two independent clauses. When you use these words, place the semicolon before the word and a comma after the word.

> *Many people travel to warm locations in the winter;* **however,** *some people really enjoy cold weather.*
>
> *The dogs obeyed their masters;* **therefore,** *they will all get a treat.*

- Use a semicolon between items in a list or series if any of the items contain commas.

> *The speakers were Dr. Judith Cornwell, English; Dr. Peter Morgan, mathematics; Dr. Shirley Englewood, history; and Dr. Charles Kreiger, science.*
>
> *I have recommended this student because she communicates well with other students, teachers, and staff; completes her assignments on time; and demonstrates an ability to organize people, materials, and projects.*

Now turn to page 224 to practice using semicolons.

Name _____

Semicolons

Practice

Rewrite each sentence correctly by putting either a semicolon or a semicolon and a comma where needed.

1. Next weekend, I plan to go hiking hiking is one of my favorite activities.

_____

2. I like to spend time outdoors I can't stand to stay inside.

_____

3. It might rain next weekend therefore I might have to stay inside.

_____

4. Craig traveled to Boise, Idaho Los Angeles, California and Nashville, Tennessee.

_____

_____

5. The Smiths went up north for their vacation the Johnsons went down south for theirs.

_____

_____

6. Emma went to Paris for her vacation it has always been her dream.

_____

7. Brianna has decided to take French lessons therefore she is reading a lot of books in French.

_____

_____

8. The flight did not include meals however we were offered free snacks.

_____

Colons

- The **colon (:)** is stronger than a comma or a semicolon.

- Use a colon to separate the hour and the minute when you write the time of day.

> 12:45   1:15   6:30

- Use a colon after the greeting of a business letter.

> *Dear Sirs:*   *Dear Mr. Franklin:*

- Use a colon after a complete sentence to introduce a list of items when introductory words such as *namely*, *for example*, or *such as* do not appear.

> *You are required to bring many items: sleeping bags, pans, and warm clothing.*
>
> *I need the following ingredients: butter, sugar, and flour.*

- Use a colon instead of a semi-colon between two sentences when the second sentence explains or illustrates the first sentence and no coordinating conjunction is being used to connect the sentences. If only one sentence follows the colon, do not capitalize the first word of the new sentence. If two or more sentences follow the colon, capitalize the first word of each sentence.

> *The news was joyous: the prince's first child had been born.*
>
> *General Smith's message was clear to his troops: Never surrender to the enemy. Protect your fellow soldiers in battle.*

Now turn to pages 226–227 to practice using colons.

6

Name _____

Colons

Practice

Rewrite each sentence below. Insert colons where needed.

1. Mr. Noble needs an assistant who can do the following tasks input data, write reports, and complete applications.

   _____

   _____

2. The movie starts at 4 45 P.M.

   _____

3. The restaurant had several house specials a hot turkey sandwich, grilled fish, mushroom soup, and raspberry cheesecake.

   _____

   _____

   _____

4. Dear Sir
   We were honored to have you come eat at our restaurant last week.

   _____

   _____

   _____

5. Every repairman must have the following tools a screwdriver, a hammer, and a saw.

   _____

   _____

Name _____

6. Everyone liked our team's new motto play your best and have fun.

_____

7. The news was shocking the tornado struck in the early morning the school had been severely damaged.

_____

_____

8. There are four seasons summer, fall, winter, and spring.

_____

Quotation Marks

- Use **quotation marks** (" ") before and after a direct quotation, the exact words that a speaker says.

  > "Someday I'm going to Brazil," said Paul.
  > "Someday," said Paul, "I'm going to Brazil."

- Use a **comma** or **commas** to separate a phrase, such as *he said*, from the quotation itself. Place the comma outside the opening quotation marks but inside the closing quotation marks.

  > Veronica asked, "Would you like to go to China?"
  > "When I get older," replied Adam, "I'd love to go there."

- Place a **period** inside closing quotation marks.

  > Pam added, "I hear Singapore is beautiful, too."

- Place a **question mark** or an **exclamation point** inside the quotation marks when it is part of the quotation.

  > "Where do you want to travel?" asked Maria.
  > "I want to go on safari in Kenya, of course!" shouted Lily.

- Use **quotation marks** around the title of a short story, song, short poem, magazine or newspaper article, and chapter of a book.

  > "Jack and the Beanstalk"   "Yankee Doodle Dandy"
  > "How Valentine's Day Came to Be" "Little Miss Muffet"
  > "Hurricane Floyd Rocks the   "A Mysterious Visitor"
  >   Southeast"

Now turn to pages 229–230 to practice using quotation marks.

Name _____

Quotation Marks

Practice

Rewrite each sentence correctly. Add punctuation where needed.

1. Are you ready for Around-the-World Day asked Mrs. Lee.

_____

2. I want to learn about Jamaica said Isabel.

_____

3. Will we asked Kevin learn about Ireland?

_____

4. Yes replied Mrs. Lee we will.

_____

5. Michael exclaimed What fun this day will be!

_____

6. Samantha and John enjoyed reading the short story Best Player.

_____

Name _____

7. Yes, it reminded me of the poem Casey at the Bat.

_____

8. It made me think of the song Take Me Out to the Ballgame.

_____

9. I read an article titled Greatest Baseball Players in History.

_____

10. Now I look for books with chapter titles such as Home Run Kings.

_____

Apostrophes

- Use an **apostrophe** and an *s* (*'s*) to form the possessive of a singular noun.

> Jason's book   my mom's bike   the car's horn

- Use an apostrophe and an *s* (*'s*) to form the possessive of a plural noun that does not end in *s*.

> children's books   men's shoes   geese's feathers

- Use an apostrophe alone to form the possessive of a plural noun that ends in *s*.

> ladies' purses   donkeys' brays   lilies' scent

- Use an apostrophe in a contraction to show where a letter or letters are missing.

> we + are = we're   he + is = he's
> would + not = wouldn't

- Do not use an apostrophe in a possessive pronoun.

> its battery   their friends   your idea

Now turn to pages 232–233 to practice using apostrophes.

Name _____

Apostrophes

Practice

Rewrite the sentences. Use apostrophes where needed.

1. Shes a great singer.

   _____

2. Have you seen Mr. Sterns golf clubs?

   _____

3. The assistants searched for the two actresses hats.

   _____

4. I asked to borrow my fathers tennis racket.

   _____

5. Sam doesnt want to go shopping today.

   _____

6. I like your suggestion, but I still cant decide what to do.

   _____

Name _____

7. Youre the best friend Ive ever had.

_____

8. The babysitter asked us to help pick up the childrens toys.

_____

9. The salesperson showed me where the ladies shoe department is.

_____

10. I love visiting my Aunt Denises house.

_____

Standard **2**

Lesson J
Titles of Works

When we write, we often mention the titles of different pieces of work. For instance, we might mention the titles of books, journals, poems, short stories, articles, chapters, songs, newspapers, or magazines. There are several different rules for how to write the titles of works.

Titles of Works

- Use **quotation marks** (" ") around the title of a short story, song, short poem, magazine or newspaper article, and chapter of a book.

"Jack and the Beanstalk"	*"Yankee Doodle Dandy"*
"How Valentine's Day Came to Be"	*"Little Miss Muffet"*
"Hurricane Floyd Rocks the Southeast"	*"A Mysterious Visitor"*

- Use **italics** or **underlining** for the title of a book, film, television series, or play. You can also use italics or underlining for the title of a magazine or newspaper.

The Secret Garden	The Secret Garden
Dumbo	Dumbo
Reading Rainbow	Reading Rainbow
Fiddler on the Roof	Fiddler on the Roof
Sports Illustrated	Sports Illustrated
The New York Times	The New York Times

Now turn to pages 235–236 to practice writing titles of works.

Name _____

Titles of Works

Practice

Rewrite each sentence correctly. Underline titles and use quotation marks for titles where needed.

1. Did you know that the movie Alice in Wonderland was based on a book?

_____

_____

2. Yes, the book was titled Alice's Adventures in Wonderland.

_____

3. My mom used to sing You Are My Sunshine to me.

_____

4. The author's life was described on a TV show called Great Authors.

_____

5. Have you read Rapunzel or other fairy tales?

_____

Name _____

6. I memorized a poem called When Pigs Fly.

_____

7. Articles about the author also appeared in newspapers such as The Chicago Tribune.

_____

8. The author's biography was published in Cricket magazine, too.

_____

9. We learned how to play Row, Row, Row Your Boat in music class.

_____

10. I wrote a short story called Mr. Gumble Fumbles.

_____

Standard 2

Lesson K
Spelling

Knowing how to spell words is an important skill to have. Sometimes spelling words can be difficult. There are strategies and tools you can use to help make spelling words easier. In this lesson you will learn more about how to improve your spelling.

Tips for Improving Spelling

Use these strategies to help you become a better speller.

- **Homophones**: Learn common homophones and make sure you have used the correct homophone in your writing.

> **They're** going to **their** house.
> They live over **there**.

- **Rhyming Words**: Think of a word you know that has the same spelling pattern as the word you want to spell, such as a rhyming word.

> tall   fall   small

- Use words that you know how to spell to help you spell new words.

> **blow + sock = block**

- Make up clues to help you remember the spelling.

> **ache = a c**at **h**as **e**ars
> **u** and **i** build a house
> a **pie**ce of **pie**
> **Al** has mor**al**s

6

- **Related Words**: Think of a related word to help you spell a word with a silent letter or a hard-to-hear sound.

> *sign—signal*
> *relative—related*

- **Syllables**: Divide the word into syllables.

> *re mind er*

- **Prefixes and Suffixes**: Learn to spell prefixes and suffixes you often use in writing.

- **Word Chunks**: Look for word chunks or smaller words that help you remember the spelling of the word.

> *together = to get her*

- Change the way you say the word to yourself to help with the spelling.

> *knife = /k nīf /*
> *beauty = /b ē ū tē /*

- **Visualizing**: Think of the times you may have seen the word in reading, on signs, or in a textbook. Try to remember how it looked. Write the word in different ways. Which one looks correct?

> ~~havy~~   ~~hevy~~   *heavy*

- **Dictionary**: Become familiar with a dictionary and use it often.
- **Personal Word List**: Keep an alphabetical Personal Word List in your Spelling Journal. Write words you have trouble spelling.

Now turn to pages 239–240 to practice using tips to help improve spelling.

Name _____

Tips for Improving Spelling Practice

Homophones:

Circle the correct word in each sentence below.

1. I bought (to, two) apples. Linda bought (two, too) apples (too, to).

Rhyming Words:

Write three words that rhyme with stew.

1. _____ **2.** _____ **3.** _____

Using Words That You Know:

Write two or more words that you know. Then try to spell a new word based on those two words.

_____ + _____ = _____

Making up Clues:

Write a clue to help you remember the spelling of the word *successful*.

_____

Related Words:

Think of a related word to help you spell the word *lovely*.

_____

Syllables:

Divide the following word into syllables to help you remember how to spell it: *industry*.

_____

Name _____

Prefixes and Suffixes:

Write three words that start with the prefix *un-*.

1. _____   2. _____   3. _____

Changing the Way You Say a Word:

Think of a different way to say the word *elephant*. Then write on the line below how you would say it.

_____

Visualizing:

Think of a word you have seen while reading. Then try to remember how it looked. On the line below, write the word in different ways and ask yourself which spelling looks correct.

_____

Using the Dictionary:

Think of a word you have seen while reading. Then use one of the strategies you learned about to try to spell it. Write the word on the line below. Then look up the spelling in the dictionary to see if you spelled it correctly.

_____

Using Resources to Check Spelling

- One way to check the spelling of unfamiliar or difficult words is in school. You can use the resources your teacher has made available. For instance, you might look at a **word wall**, which is usually a large chart that has vocabulary words or other difficult words listed on it. You might also look at **posters**, **charts**, and **pictures** that are displayed in your classroom.

- You can also use a **dictionary** to look up misspelled words or words that are difficult to spell. To look up a word in the dictionary, you need to know what letter or letters the word starts with. You can use the spelling strategies you learned about to help you start to spell the word. For instance, you can practice visualizing the word or dividing the word into syllables. Once you have the beginning of the word sounded out, use the dictionary to check the spelling.

- If you are working on a computer, use the spell-check program. Remember, though, that spell-checkers are not perfect. If you write *your* instead of *you're*, a spell-checker will not catch the mistake. Always check your work after using the spell-check program.

- Another resource you can use to check the spelling of words is a word list. To create a word list, write down words you find difficult to spell. You might use a notebook or a set of note cards to create this resource. You can organize your words by alphabet or by a spelling rule.

Now turn to page 242 to practice using resources to check spelling.

6

Name _____

Using Resources to Check Spelling

Practice

Write on the lines below any words that you have trouble spelling. You can look up the words in a dictionary or write them when you see them spelled correctly. Continue to add words to this list and use it as a reference when you're writing.

_____

_____

_____

_____

_____

_____

_____

_____

_____

_____

_____

_____

_____

_____

_____

_____

_____

_____

_____

_____

Spelling Commonly Confused Words Correctly

The English language includes some confusing words that are often misused. The following charts will help you understand how to use these words properly.

Words	Correct Usage
lay	*Lay* means "to put something down." **Lay** *the papers on my desk.*
lie	*Lie* means "to recline or rest." *Seth* **lies** *on the floor in front of the fireplace.*
loose	*Loose* means "not secured." *Maggie had her first* **loose** *tooth.*
lose	*Lose* means "to misplace." It is a verb. *Did you* **lose** *your house key?*
set	*Set* means "to put something down or in a certain place." *I* **set** *my pencil on the table.*
sit	*Sit* means "to be seated." *Our class should* **sit** *in the front of the auditorium.*
their	*Their* is a possessive pronoun meaning "belonging to them." *The Murphys are gone, so Ryan will feed* **their** *dog.*
they're	*They're* is a contraction meaning "they are." *We aren't sure when* **they're** *coming back from vacation.*
your	*Your* is a possessive pronoun that means "something that belongs to you." *Is that* **your** *cat?*
you're	*You're* is the contraction for "you are." **You're** *a wonderful artist, Sam.*
whose	*Whose* is an adjective showing possession. **Whose** *paper is this on the floor?*
who's	*Who's* is a contraction for "who is." The apostrophe takes the place of the *i* in *is*. *I don't know* **who's** *coming to the festival next week.*

6

- Some words are easily confused because they sound the same.
- Some words are easily confused because they are spelled similarly or because they sound alike. These words have different definitions, so you need to be sure you use the correct one.

accept except	any more anymore	desert dessert	loose lose	taut taunt
accuse excuse	approve improve	expect suspect	midst mist	than then
adapt adopt	breath breathe	farther further	personal personnel	though through
afar affair	cloth clothe	finale finally	picture pitcher	very vary
alley ally	close clothes	formally formerly	quiet quite	weather whether
all ready already	conscience conscious	hour our	recent resent	your you're
all together altogether	costume custom	later latter	respectively respectfully	
angel angle	dairy diary	lay lie	sink zinc	

Now turn to page 245 to practice spelling commonly confused words correctly.

Name _____

Spelling Commonly Confused Words Correctly

Practice

Write a story about a real or imaginary holiday celebration. Use some problem words and some easily confused words in your story. Underline each problem word and easily confused word you use, and check to be sure you have used and spelled it correctly.

_____

_____

_____

_____

_____

_____

_____

_____

_____

_____

_____

_____

_____

_____

_____

_____

_____

_____

_____

_____

Lesson A
Use Precise Language

Good writers and effective speakers choose their words very carefully so that they can precisely describe an idea or a topic. Word choice can have a powerful effect on a spoken or written message.

In fact, Mark Twain, a famous American writer, described it this way. He said, "The difference between the almost right word and the right word is really a large matter—it's the difference between the lightning bug and the lightning." So if you want to put a little "lightning" in your speaking and writing, think carefully about your choice of words.

Use Precise Language: Model

Compare these paragraphs. Which paragraph describes the scene more precisely?

> The sky looked cloudy, and then lots of rain fell down. Our clothes got wet because we didn't have umbrellas. We walked in puddles even though we weren't wearing boots. By the time the sun came out, we felt great. The flowers looked prettier after the rain.

> The sky looked ominous, and then buckets of rain poured down. Our clothes got drenched because we didn't have umbrellas. We splashed in shining puddles even though we weren't wearing boots. By the time the sun emerged from the clouds, we felt refreshed. The flowers looked as though they had drunk their fill of rain.

The words the writer chose for the second paragraph are more vivid, and they describe the storm, the actions of the narrator, and other details more precisely. These word choices help readers picture the events.

Now look carefully at the words that tell the actions. Compare the word choices. Why is the word *poured* a more effective word choice than *fell*? Look at these other instances in the paragraphs where the words and phrases mean the same thing but are more precise and vivid in the second paragraph.

> The sky looked <u>cloudy</u>, and then <u>lots</u> of rain <u>fell</u> down. Our clothes got <u>wet</u> because we didn't have umbrellas. We <u>walked</u> in puddles even though we weren't wearing boots. By the time the sun <u>came out</u>, we felt <u>great</u>. The flowers looked <u>prettier</u> <u>after the</u> rain.

> The sky looked <u>ominous</u>, and then <u>buckets</u> of rain <u>poured</u> down. Our clothes got <u>drenched</u> because we didn't have umbrellas. We <u>splashed</u> in <u>shining</u> puddles even though we weren't wearing boots. By the time the sun <u>emerged from the</u> <u>clouds</u>, we felt <u>refreshed</u>. The flowers looked <u>as though they</u> <u>had drunk their fill of</u> rain.

Now turn to page 248 to practice using precise language.

Name _____

Use Precise Language

Practice

Read the sentences below. Then revise the sentences by replacing the underlined words with more precise language. Write your answers on the lines.

1. My friend <u>laughed</u> at my joke.

   _____

2. The <u>small</u> ants worked together to get food.

   _____

3. The <u>big</u> building on the corner is new.

   _____

4. The <u>pretty</u> garden is full of tulips.

   _____

5. The judges <u>gave</u> prizes to each participant.

   _____

6. We <u>walked</u> along the seashore.

   _____

7. The horses <u>ran</u> to the barn for their dinner.

   _____

8. The <u>good</u> vegetable stew took an hour to make.

   _____

9. It is a <u>nice</u> day for a picnic.

   _____

10. Mom <u>told</u> us to be home by three o'clock.

   _____

Lesson B
Choose Punctuation for Effect

Punctuation is like road signs for written language. It lets readers know such things as when to stop, when to pause, and what the exact words of a speaker are. We follow the rules for using punctuation so our readers can clearly understand our writing.

But did you know that punctuation can also be used for effect? When we write, we can use punctuation to show emotion or to create a desired tone.

Choose Punctuation for Effect: Model

- Use **parentheses** around material that is added to a sentence but is not important to the meaning of the sentence.

> *There were all sorts of treats (including my favorite cookies) at the bake sale.*

- Put punctuation inside the parentheses when it goes with the information inside.

> *Mom ate every single brussels sprout (I didn't even know she liked them!) on her plate last night.*

- Put punctuation outside the parentheses when it goes with the main part of the sentence.

> *My dentist told me that I have no cavities (fortunately).*

- Use a **dash** to add emphasis to your writing. A dash is a mark of separation. It is stronger than a comma and less formal than parentheses.

> *Try this apple—you'll like it.*
>
> *She needs to go to the grocery store—tomorrow, if possible— to buy more yogurt.*

- An **interjection** is a word or a phrase that shows emotion.
- Use a comma to separate interjections from the rest of a sentence.

> *Yes, she loves to read!*

- If the interjection shows a very strong emotion, use an exclamation mark.

> *Hooray! They won the game!*

Now turn to page 251 to practice choosing punctuation for effect.

Name _____

Choose Punctuation for Effect
Practice

A. Proofread the sentences. Add parentheses ( ) once in each numbered item.

1. Please enter the building through the side door the front door is locked.

2. I recited the whole poem it's very long from memory.

3. Did you get your invitation the one to Tara's birthday party yesterday?

4. We have to wear costumes scary ones only to the party.

5. Eat an apple any variety you like every day because it is good for you.

6. I found out Did you already know? that the picnic is tomorrow.

7. Each color of the rainbow there are seven colors comes from white light.

8. Look both ways right and left before crossing the street.

B. Fix the sentences. Add commas after the interjections and dashes where needed.

1. No there is no such thing as a leprechaun.

2. Good I had hoped we wouldn't have to go swimming on such a cold day.

3. Many years ago ten in fact we moved to a new state.

4. There is much to learn about the wildlife in the forest it will be exciting to study their habits.

5. Two winners one boy and one girl took prizes at the spelling bee.

6. My grandmother preserved most of the old family photos luckily.

7. Yes the teacher will let us study in groups for the test.

8. The amusement park was very exciting it had four roller coasters.

9. Wow I can't believe this great news!

10. Monday and maybe Tuesday should be good days for walking in the park.

Lesson C
Effective Sentences

Effective sentences are the building blocks of clear communication. To be truly effective, however, sentences must also be interesting to your readers or listeners.

You can make your sentences more powerful in several ways. You can **expand** them by adding information and details. You can **combine** them by putting two or more sentences together. Finally, you can **reduce** them by shortening them—where appropriate—to produce a certain effect.

Use Effective Sentences: Model

Look at these models of how to expand, combine, and reduce sentences in order to make them more effective.

Expand

Use descriptive language to expand your sentences and make them more interesting and meaningful to readers.

> **Original:** *The girl walked home from school.*
>
> **Revised:** *The tired girl trudged home after an exhausting day at school.*

Combine Sentences

Use commas and **conjunctions** to create **compound and complex sentences**.

Conjunctions

A **conjunction** joins words or groups of words. *And, but,* and *or* are conjunctions.

Some conjunctions tell *where, when, why, how,* or *under what conditions*. These conjunctions include *after, although, as, because, before, if, since, so that, until, when, whether,* and *while*.

Compound and Complex Sentences

A sentence that contains two or more simple sentences joined by *and*, *but*, or *or* is called a **compound sentence**. In a compound sentence, a comma is placed before the conjunction.

A sentence that contains an independent clause and one or more dependent clauses is called a **complex sentence**. In a complex sentence, the independent clause and the dependent clause or clauses are joined by a conjunction other than *and*, *but*, or *or*. These conjunctions include *after*, *although*, *as*, *because*, *before*, *if*, *since*, *so that*, *until*, *when*, *whether*, and *while*. The conjunction can appear at the beginning of the sentence or in the middle of the sentence.

> **Original:** Tiny bonsai trees may look like young plants. They are fully grown.
>
> **Revised:** Tiny bonsai trees may look like young plants, but they are fully grown.
>
> **Original:** The moon does not have an atmosphere. There is no wind to blow the footprints away.
>
> **Revised:** Since the moon does not have an atmosphere, there is no wind to blow the footprints away.

Reduce

Have you ever heard the saying, "The less said, the better"? While details can be interesting, sometimes they get in the way of a sentence's meaning. Pare down, or shorten, sentences, where appropriate, to make them more powerful.

> **Original:** The apple, being tart, caused him to wince when he bit into it.
>
> **Revised:** He winced when he bit into the tart apple.

Now turn to pages 254–255 to practice writing more effective sentences by expanding, combining, and reducing them.

6

Name _____

Effective Sentences

Practice

A. Expand the sentences below to add meaning and to make them more interesting. Rewrite the expanded sentences on the lines. The words in parentheses may help you.

1. The mouse ran toward the cheese. (tiny, scampered, tempting)

_____

2. We shook in the cold lake. (shivered, uncontrollably, freezing)

_____

3. I ate the peach. (sweet, juicy, eagerly)

_____

4. The redwood stood tall. (enormous, towered, above the other trees)

_____

5. I was surprised to find money. (astonished, ten dollars, in my pocket)

_____

B. Combine each pair of sentences, using the conjunction in parentheses. Write the new sentence on the lines.

1. They tasted space food. They wore space suits. (and)

_____

_____

2. Gum and drinks are not allowed. They can create disasters in the dirt-free zone. (because)

_____

_____

Name _____

3. The students were told to remove their jewelry. They would not be injured. (so that)

_____

_____

4. The trainer would hold onto the chair. The last student had a turn. (until)

_____

_____

5. He volunteered to sit in the gravity chair. He realized how hard it was to move around. (before)

_____

_____

C. **Read the sentence pairs below. Circle the letter of the sentence that is more effective.**

1. a. Our car is not working, so we had to bring it to the shop and take the bus instead.

   b. We took the bus because our car is in the shop.

2. a. The fashionable suit fit well.

   b. The suit was fashionable and felt like a good fit.

3. a. The toddler, who was angry, picked up his toy, which was blue, and threw it.

   b. The angry toddler picked up his blue toy and threw it.

4. a. I really like books that involve mysteries more than any other kind of book.

   b. My favorite books involve mysteries.

5. a. You could tell that Jack and Jill disagreed because he nodded and she shook her head.

   b. Jack nodded, but Jill shook her head.

Standard 3.b

Standard
3.b

Lesson D
Compare Language Use

We speak and write differently depending on the situation. We adjust our levels of language depending on our audience and our reason for communicating. In this lesson you will learn different ways we use language, including the following.

- Formal English
- Informal English
- Dialect
- Register

Formal English

We use **Formal English** when we are requesting information from a business or from someone we don't know.

Formal English is used mainly in writing and in some speaking situations. This style of English has a more serious tone and is commonly used in reports, essays, and business letters as well as in conversations with people we may know but with whom we are not close friends.

- Formal English uses more complex vocabulary than informal English. It uses words that you probably wouldn't use in a regular conversation with a friend.

- When formal English is used in writing, sentences are usually longer and more complex than those you would use when writing to a friend.

- People also use formal English when speaking in formal situations, such as during a job interview or when talking to the school principal.

Read the following example of a business letter.

Formal English: Model

12 Graydale Street
Cincinnati, OH
September 15, 1878

Mr. Thomas Jones, Editor-in-Chief
Cincinnati Daily Gazette
350 Main Street
Cincinnati, OH

Dear Mr. Jones:

The Constitution states that everyone has certain basic rights, and our laws are built on the idea of equality. However, many Americans still are not treated equally. Women are still not allowed to vote!

I appeal to the conscience of all people. You can change this! We can take a great step together toward equality for all Americans. Please act to give women the legal right to vote.

Sincerely,

Emily James

Now turn to pages 258–259 to practice using Formal English.

6

Name _____

Formal English

Practice

Write a business letter about an issue that concerns you. You may change any of the information below. Make sure you use formal language in your letter.

123 Cedar Lane
Palatine, IL 60067
November 15, 2011

Ms. Harriet Harrison, Park Ranger
Blue Waters National Park
4321 Aquamarine Way
Crystal, CA 95389

Dear Ms. Harrison:

_____

_____

_____

_____

_____

_____

_____

_____

_____

_____

_____

Name _____

_____

_____

_____

_____

_____

_____

_____

_____

_____

Sincerely,

Rob Robertson

Informal English

People often use **Informal English** when they are speaking to friends and family. People also use informal English when they write e-mails, notes, and letters to people they know.

- When people write using informal English, they use everyday vocabulary and sometimes include expressions and slang that are common where they live. For instance, in informal English, a writer might use the word *stuff* to describe something he or she found rather than a specific name for it.

- Personal pronouns, such as *I*, *you*, and *we*, are often used in informal English to create a more personal style. Contractions, such as *it's* instead of *it is*, are also commonly used in informal English.

Read the following example of an informal e-mail sent to a group.

Informal English: Model

Hi, everyone!

I made it—I'm here with the hiking team in Colorado! One thing I learned right away is to put on my sunglasses before going outside. The glare of sunlight off the snow-covered mountain is very powerful!

This afternoon our guides are going to teach us about altitude sickness. Some of Colorado's highest peaks are more than 14,000 feet—more than two miles up. Can you believe it? I thought that the cold air and snow would be the main problem! I've heard that headaches and nausea are symptoms of altitude sickness. One thing that helps is to drink lots of water. You all know I can do that!

I'll e-mail again tomorrow!

Stacy

Now turn to page 261 to practice using informal English.

Name _____

Informal English

Practice

Write an e-mail to a friend. Tell your friend about what you did over the weekend. Make sure you use informal language in your e-mail.

_____

_____

_____

_____

_____

_____

_____

_____

_____

_____

Dialect

Both formal and informal English may vary in dialect. **Dialect** usually refers to regional differences in language. Where we live can affect the vocabulary, pronunciation, and even grammar we use when speaking or writing.

Read the two versions of the poem below. Note the "cowboy" dialect used in the second version.

Dialect: Model

Balloon Flight

It floats in the air
like a bird's loosened feather,
drifting among blue.

Unlike a feather,
it is guided by someone
who chooses its course.

Balloon A-Flyin'

See the balloon floatin' up yonder?
Kinda reminds me of a little birdie's feather
A-driftin' on the ocean.

But balloons and feathers are different, see.
A feather is as free as a cowboy on the range
But a balloon is guided like a horse on a rope.

Think about how you would describe each dialect and the differences between them.

Now turn to pages 263–264 to compare language use.

Name _____

Dialect

Practice

Read the following passage containing dialect. On the lines below the passage, rewrite it using formal English. Then answer the question.

> Ol' Febold, he spied a wagon train headed his way. He ran to the road and started wavin' his hat in the air like a madman, he was that glad ter see folks.
>
> The wagon train folks waved back, and soon they were ridin' their wagons right on up to ol' Febold.
>
> "Is there gold in this-here state?" one of the wagon-train folks asked.
>
> "We've got somethin' here in Nebraska that's way better'n gold," said Febold.
>
> "What's that you say?" another member of the wagon train asked.
>
> "Why, we've got hundreds of acres of the best prairie land in the whole wide world, just itchin' to be farmed," Febold answered.
>
> The folks in the wagon train looked at the dry land around them, peered up at the sky (where there was nary a raincloud), and started laughin' their heads off.

_____

_____

_____

_____

_____

_____

_____

_____

Name _____

_____

_____

_____

_____

_____

_____

_____

_____

_____

Describe how the dialect in the original passage is different than the formal language in your version.

_____

_____

_____

_____

Register

Dialect variations depend on who is using them. **Register**, however, varies according to the use of the language itself. Register refers to the way language is used in different contexts, or situations, when speaking or writing.

Read the two dramatic excerpts below. Because the social contexts, or situations, are different, the speakers' register changes. Informal terms and forms of address are used in the first excerpt, a casual conversation between young friends. But when the conversation involves a teacher, more formal words and sentences are used.

Register: Model

> *The first day of a new school year. MALIA, ten years old, is almost at school when she sees her classmate NOAH.*
>
> MALIA: Hey, Noah!
>
> NOAH: What's up, Malia?
>
> MALIA: Nobody saw you all summer!
>
> NOAH: Yeah, 'cause I was in New Zealand—
>
> MALIA: Huh? New Zealand? Where's that?
>
> NOAH: By Australia.
>
> MALIA: Why'd you go there?
>
> NOAH: My dad had a job there and decided my whole family should go.
>
> MALIA: Oh. Cool.

The fifth-graders are at their desks and listening to the teacher, who is standing at the front of the room.

MS. PATEL: Good morning, everyone, and welcome to fifth grade! We are going to learn a lot from each other this year. Before we start our journey, would anyone like to share what they did this summer? *(NOAH raises his hand.)* Yes, Noah?

NOAH: I went with my family to New Zealand.

MS. PATEL: My goodness! New Zealand! Class, can any of you tell me where New Zealand is? *(MALIA raises her hand, smiling at Noah.)* Yes, Malia?

MALIA: It's near Australia!

MS. PATEL: Very good! Noah, how did your family come to be in New Zealand?

NOAH: My dad got a summer job working on Franz Josef Glacier. He's a scientist.

MS. PATEL: That's wonderful! We are going to be learning about glaciers and other geologic formations this year. Perhaps your father can be one of our guest lecturers!

Think about how the words and sentences changed when Noah and Malia began to talk to their teacher in the classroom.

Now turn to pages 267–268 to practice comparing language use.

Name _____

Register

Practice

Read the following passage, noting the register of a typical family conversation between adults and children. On the lines that follow the passage, rewrite it in a register that you would use while talking with a good friend in the cafeteria at school. Then answer the question.

> *A family is seated around a table having dinner. The family includes Mom, GRANDMA, and ten-year-old MARISOL.*
>
> **Mom:** Would anyone like more mashed potatoes? No? Well, there's more if you change your minds! So, Marisol, what was school like today? Did your teacher give your science tests back?
>
> **Marisol:** Oh, school was okay, Mom. We did get our tests back.
>
> **Grandma:** Did you get an A, Marisol? You studied so hard!
>
> **Marisol:** (*smiling*): Yes, Grandma. Thank you for helping me study! Mr. Coban wrote a note on my test—look, here it is . . .
>
> **Grandma:** "Congratulations on a job well done!" Oh, Marisol, that's great!
>
> **Mom:** I think you—and your best study partner, your grandmother— have earned some extra ice cream for dessert tonight!

_____

_____

_____

_____

_____

_____

_____

_____

_____

Name _____

_____

_____

_____

_____

_____

_____

_____

_____

_____

_____

How are the registers of the two conversations—the original and your revision—similar and different?

_____

_____

_____

_____

Lesson A
Multiple-Meaning Words

A **multiple-meaning word** is a word that has more than one meaning. Though the word's meaning, part of speech, and pronunciation may change according to how it is used in a sentence, the spelling of the word stays the same.

A **homonym** is one example of a multiple-meaning word. Homonyms are words that are spelled and pronounced the same but are different in meaning.

A **homograph** is another example of a multiple-meaning word. Homographs are words that are spelled the same but have different meanings and origins. They may also have different pronunciations.

You can use a dictionary to find all the meanings and pronunciations of a word. Then you can use context clues to choose the correct meaning of the word as it is used in a sentence.

Homonyms

Read the following sentence pairs, looking closely at the underlined homonyms.

1. Be careful not to <u>jam</u> your finger in the door when you shut it.

   Would you like strawberry <u>jam</u> on your peanut butter sandwich?

The word *jam* is spelled and pronounced the same in both sentences, but its meaning is different. In the first sentence, *jam* is a verb that means "crush." In the second sentence, *jam* is a noun that means "a thick spread made of fruit and sugar."

2. <u>Close</u> the gate so the dog does not run out of the yard.

   The center will <u>close</u> due to lack of funds.

In the first sentence, the fact that there is a gate that keeps the dog in the yard helps you understand that *close* means "shut." In the second sentence, "lack of funds" gives you the clue that here *close* means "shut down" or "end."

3. We planted the carrots in a straight <u>row</u> from one end of the garden to the other.

We will <u>row</u> the boat faster if we use better oars.

In the first sentence, "straight" and "from one end . . . to the other" are clues that *row* means "line." In the second sentence, you can see that *row* refers to the action of using oars to move a boat.

Homographs

Read the following sentences. Note the underlined homographs.

1. He will <u>present</u> the necklace as a <u>present</u> to his mother on Mother's Day.

The first *present* is a verb meaning "give," and the second *present* is a noun meaning "gift." The two words have different pronunciations, too.

2. I will <u>lead</u> you to the park if you don't know how to get there.

Did you know that <u>lead</u> and other heavy metals are poisonous?

In the first sentence, "if you don't know how to get there" gives you the clue that *lead* is a verb that means "guide" or "show." In the second sentence, "and other heavy metals" tells you that here *lead* is a noun that refers to a kind of metal. These two words are also pronounced in different ways.

3. That horse can jump high enough to <u>vault</u> over a ten-foot fence!

The bank employees will put your money in a secure <u>vault</u>.

In the first sentence, "jump high" and "over a . . . fence" tell you that *vault* is a verb meaning "jump." The second sentence shows you that *vault* can also be a noun meaning "place for storing valuable items." *Vault* is pronounced the same in both sentences.

Multiple-Meaning Word: Model

When you find a **multiple-meaning word**, you can use a graphic organizer to write down all the meanings of the word that you know or that you find in a dictionary. Note the part of speech for each meaning. Then try each meaning in the sentence to find the one that best fits the context. In the example below, the third meaning matches the use of the underlined word in the sentence.

We pulled the boat up onto the <u>bank</u> of the river.

bank	
Meaning	**Part of Speech**
a business that keeps money for people or other companies	noun
to put money into a bank	verb
a steep side of a river, lake, or stream	noun
to tilt or angle an airplane or a car	verb

In the sentence above, the word *bank* matches the third meaning: a steep side of a river, lake, or stream.

Now turn to pages 272–273 to practice using multiple-meaning words.

Name _____

Multiple-Meaning Words

Practice

A. Read the sentences. Use a dictionary to find homonyms for the boldfaced words. Write each meaning and its part of speech in a separate chart row. Then put an X next to the meaning that best fits the sentence. The first one has been done for you.

1. The lawyer asked the witness to describe the **state** of the vehicle after the accident.

state	
Meaning	**Part of Speech**
_____ an area that is part of a country	noun
____X____ the condition of something	noun
_____ to express in words	verb

2. Four thin posts were the only things left to **support** the house.

support	
Meaning	**Part of Speech**
_____	noun
_____	noun
_____	verb

Name _____

3. In New Mexico, I visited a Spanish mission built in the 1600s.

mission	
Meaning	**Part of Speech**
_____	noun
_____	noun
_____	verb

B. **Use a dictionary to find the meanings of the following homographs. Then write a sentence for each meaning of the word.**

1. contest (noun) _____

contest (verb) _____

2. protest (noun) _____

protest (verb) _____

3. contract (noun) _____

contract (verb) _____

4. toll (noun) _____

toll (verb) _____

5. bass (noun) _____

bass (noun) _____

Lesson B
Use Context Clues

Context clues can help you figure out the meaning of a word or phrase you don't know. These clues can be found in the words and sentences surrounding the unknown word or phrase.

Sometimes a writer uses **signal words** that indicate a certain type of context clue. You will learn to recognize different types of context clues you might come across as you read.

Recognize Context Clues: Model

The chart below shows different types of context clues you might come across as you read.

Definitions	Words such as *means* or *is* may signal a definition.
	word: *bicameral* — The U.S. Congress is bicameral, which <u>means it has two chambers or houses.</u>
Examples	*Such as* and *other* may signal examples.
	word: *obligations* — Council members have many obligations, <u>such as going to meetings and reading about laws.</u>
Restatements	Look for signal words such as *which is* and *or*.
	word: *flawless* — The insect's camouflage was flawless, <u>or perfect.</u>
Cause/Effect Relationships	*Because*, *so that*, and *in order* to signal a cause/effect relationship.
	word: *surrender* — The army had to surrender <u>because the other side won.</u>

Comparisons	*Like, unlike, but, not, in contrast to, similar to,* and *in the same way* signal a comparison in the text.
	Word: ecstatic Voters in this state were ecstatic about the result of the election, <u>unlike</u> the <u>unhappy</u> voters in the other states.

Definitions

Look at the underlined words and phrases in the model sentences. The underlined word is defined by the underlined phrase that follows. Signal words for definitions include *is* and *means.*

> A <u>coward</u> is <u>someone who is not brave.</u>
>
> The fact that the spy used an <u>alias</u> means he used <u>a name made up to conceal identity.</u>
>
> A <u>congregation</u> is <u>a gathering of people or things.</u>

Examples

Look at the underlined words or phrases in the model sentences. The second underlined phrase gives an **example** of the first underlined word or words. Some words that signal examples are *such as, other, include, these,* and *for example.*

> The city government is responsible for <u>municipal activities,</u> such as <u>keeping the streets clean and hosting public events.</u>
>
> <u>Platinum</u> and other <u>precious metals</u> are used to make jewelry.
>
> My parents consider some expenses <u>extravagant</u>; for example, they think it is <u>wasteful</u> to spend money on video games.

6

Restatements

Look at the underlined words or phrases in the model sentences. The second underlined phrases are **restatements** of the first underlined words. Words that signal restatements include *or, that is, in other words,* and *which is*.

> The mayor wanted time to <u>contemplate</u>, or <u>think about</u>, his decision before announcing it.
>
> I want to become an <u>entomologist</u>, which is a <u>person who studies insects</u>.
>
> Lara <u>was a dragon</u>—that is, she <u>got very angry</u>—if anyone tried to bully her little brother.

Cause/Effect Relationships

Look at the underlined words or phrases in the model sentences. The second underlined word or phrase shows a **cause/effect relationship** to the first underlined words. Signal words for cause/effect relationships include *because, so that,* and *in order to*.

> I had to <u>mediate</u> the argument between my friends in order to <u>help them come to an agreement</u>.
>
> Because Greg <u>could not decide which college to attend</u>, he found himself in a <u>dilemma</u>.
>
> It was <u>difficult to see</u> the trail because <u>the blanket of night had fallen</u> over the woods.

Comparisons

Look at the underlined words in the model sentences. The second word shows a **comparison** to the first. Signal words for comparisons include *like, unlike, but, not, in contrast to, similar to,* and *in the same way.*

> The students at our school are <u>zealous</u> about community issues, unlike the <u>uninterested</u> students at my friend's school.
>
> In contrast to my brother, who is <u>enthusiastic</u> about eating meat, I am <u>reluctant</u> to eat animals.
>
> Someday people may <u>colonize</u> the moon, just like our ancestors first <u>settled</u> America.

Now turn to pages 278–280 to practice using context clues.

Name _____

Use Context Clues
Practice
Definitions

Circle the words in each sentence that define the underlined word.

1. Someone who is <u>flexible</u> is someone who can adapt and change.

2. Seed <u>dispersal</u> is the scattering of seeds by birds and other animals.

3. The leader of our state is the <u>governor</u>.

4. An <u>auditorium</u> is a place where people listen to speakers.

5. The musicians know how to <u>collaborate</u>, meaning they know how to work together.

Examples

Circle the words in each sentence that serve as examples of the underlined word.

1. We volunteer for <u>charities</u>, such as the American Red Cross, to help people in need.

2. Our bodies need many <u>nutrients</u>, including vitamins and minerals.

3. Lava from a volcano is made of rock, metal, gas, and other <u>substances</u>.

4. The towns are separated by natural <u>boundaries</u> that include a river and a forest.

5. American colonists had many different <u>occupations</u>, such as blacksmithing and carpentry.

Common Core State Standards Literacy Handbook

Name _____

Restatements

A. Circle the words in each sentence that serve as restatements of the underlined word.

1. The state legislators, or lawmakers, supported the governor's plan.

2. The students wanted the opportunity, or chance, to discuss the book.

3. The music teacher started an orchestra, or music group, this year.

B. Complete each sentence below by restating the underlined word. You may use a dictionary to help you.

1. She is a volunteer at the hospital; in other words, she works _____.

2. George Washington defied, or _____, the British rule of the colonies.

Cause/Effect Relationships

Circle the words in each sentence that show a cause/effect relationship to the underlined word.

1. John was anxious about moving to another state because he was nervous about living in a new place.

2. Her face wrinkled as she laughed, so that her cheeks scrunched up and lines appeared at the corners of her eyes.

3. Grandfather said that the code was a triumph because each message was sent and received with success.

4. Because autumn arrived, the leaves of the trees began to wither.

5. We repeated the lesson over and over so that it would be easy to remember.

Name _____

Comparisons

A. Circle the words in each sentence that show a comparison to the underlined word.

1. Dermont was <u>forlorn</u> when he first left home for camp, but soon he was hopeful that he would enjoy the summer.

2. Colonists with different religions were treated fairly, unlike in their home countries, where they were often <u>persecuted</u>.

3. I wanted my art project to look <u>remarkable</u>, not ordinary.

B. Complete each sentence below to show a comparison to the underlined word. You may use a dictionary to help you.

1. The <u>fierceness</u> of lions is in contrast to the _____ of cows.

2. The new mattress was <u>supple</u>, not _____ like the old one.

Standard
4.b

Lesson C
Understand Word Parts

Many English words are formed by adding prefixes and suffixes to a root word. Prefixes, suffixes, and roots often come from Latin and Greek.

A **prefix** is a word part that is added to the *beginning* of a word to change its meaning.

A **suffix** is a word part that is added to the *end* of a word to change its meaning.

The **root** of a word is its *basic meaning* before a prefix or a suffix is added to it.

Prefixes

A **prefix** is a word part that is added to the beginning of a word to change its meaning. The chart shows some common Latin and Greek prefixes and their meanings.

Latin Prefix	Meaning	Greek Prefix	Meaning
re-	back, again	*para-*	beside, beyond
non-	not	*mono-*	one
co-	with	*syn-*	with, same

Read the sentences below. The meaning of each underlined word can be determined by thinking about the meaning of the prefix.

When I finish college, I would like to be a paramedic.

Paramedic literally means "beside medic." A paramedic is someone who works beside, or assists, a medical person.

The coauthors wrote the book together.

Coauthors are authors who work with each other to author, or write, a book.

The twins in my class are nonidentical.

Nonidentical means "not identical." When you know that *identical* means "alike," you understand that these twins do not look alike.

Now turn to page 283 to practice using what you know about prefixes.

Name _____

Prefixes

Practice

Read each sentence. Use what you know about prefixes to write the meaning of each boldfaced word. Write your answers on the lines.

1. You need to **review** your notes before the test. _____

2. Roy would rather read a **nonfiction** journal article than a novel. _____

3. The **paralegal** helped the lawyer prepare her case. _____

4. My dad and my brother **comanage** our family business. _____

5. The words *habitat* and *home* are **synonyms.** _____

6. The speaker droned on in an unbearable **monotone.** _____

7. I missed the goalie's save, so I watched the onscreen **replay.** _____

8. The neighbors decided to **cohost** a block party. _____

9. That **nonabsorbent** cloth does not work for cleaning up spills. _____

10. You may have taken a train, but have you ever taken a **monorail?** _____

Suffixes

A **suffix** is a word part that is added to the end of a word to change its meaning. The chart shows some common Latin and Greek suffixes and their meanings.

Latin Suffix	Meaning		Greek Prefix	Meaning
-able/-ible	able to, worthy of		*-log/-logue*	to speak
-al	like, relating to		*-sis*	process, action

Two suffixes that come from both Latin and Greek are *-y* and *-ity*. These suffixes both mean "having the quality of; state of."

Read each sentence. The meaning of each underlined word can be determined by thinking about the meaning of the suffix.

> Handle that <u>breakable</u> dish with extra care.

Breakable means "able to break." Something that is breakable is fragile and likely to break easily.

> Her <u>musical</u> voice is a pleasure to hear.

Because *-al* means "like," a musical voice is a voice that sounds like music.

> <u>Reality</u> can be stranger than make-believe.

When you think about how *-ity* means "state of," you see that *reality* means "the state of the real." Reality, then, is real life.

For more information about **suffixes,** go to Foundational Skills 3.1 Lesson A **Word Parts: Suffixes** on page 248 in Volume 1.

Now turn to page 285 to practice using what you know about suffixes.

Name _____

Suffixes

Practice

A. Look at the boldfaced phrases. Use what you know about suffixes to write one word that will complete each sentence. The first one has been done for you.

1. **A solution that has sense** is _____ sensible _____.

2. **A person who has honor** is _____.

3. **A tool that people are able to use** is _____.

4. **Something that is able to be converted** is _____.

5. **Someone worthy of admiration** is _____.

B. Underline the suffix in each word below. Then write the meaning of each word on the lines provided.

1. normal _____

2. collapsible _____

3. comfortable _____

4. monologue _____

5. civility _____

Roots

The **root** of a word is its basic meaning before a prefix or a suffix is added to it. If you know the spellings and meanings of roots, you can figure out how to spell and define words that contain them. Here are some common Latin and Greek roots and their meanings.

Latin Root	Meaning	Greek Root	Meaning
dict	speak	*astr*	star
sci	know	*photo*	light
san	health	*gen*	birth
aud	hear	*chron*	time
spect	look	*graph*	write, record

Read the sentences below. The meaning of each underlined word can be determined by thinking about the meaning of its root.

> Jahara likes to watch the game and be a spectator rather than actually playing.

Spectator, containing the root *spect,* means "a person who watches."

> You must have good diction if you want to hold the attention of those listening to you.

Diction, containing the root *dict,* means "expression; pronunciation." Someone who has good diction speaks clearly.

> Mom thinks her musical achievements are the result of genetics—as well as hard work—because her parents are accomplished musicians, too.

You have learned that the root *gen* means "birth." Think about the context clue that Mom's parents are also accomplished musicians. Things that are a result of genetics are things that people are born with.

For more information about **roots,** go to Foundational Skills 3.1 Lesson A **Word Parts: Roots** on page 256 in Volume 1.

Turn to pages 287–288 to practice using what you know about word roots.

Name _____

Roots

Practice

A. Use the chart below to help you choose the word in parentheses that is being described. Write the correct word on the line.

Latin Root	Meaning	Greek Root	Meaning
dict	speak	*astr*	star
sci	know	*photo*	light
san	health	*gen*	birth
aud	hear	*chron*	time
spect	look	*graph*	write, record

1. This is a noun that means "the time order in which events occur."

(chronology, covert) _____

2. This is the study of the history of births in families.

(pharmacology, genealogy) _____

3. This is a large building or room where people listen to concerts.

(auditorium, concerto) _____

4. This adjective means "awake and able to think and know."

(conscious, determined) _____

5. This adjective means "free from germs that cause illness."

(laundered, sanitary) _____

Name _____

6. This is the study of objects in space.

(anthropology, astronomy) _____

7. This is recorded using the action of light on film.

(photograph, photogenic) _____

B. Look at the word *photosynthesis.* You can see that it is made from the following Greek word parts:

Root	Meaning	Prefix	Meaning	Suffix	Meaning
photo	light	*syn*	with, same	*sis*	process, action

Now look at the definitions below. Use your knowledge of word parts to select the correct definition of photosynthesis. Circle your answer.

a. a copy of printed material made through the action of light

b. the process of how plants make food with the aid of light

c. an instrument used for measuring the intensity of light

Lesson D
Use Print and Digital Resources

Reference materials are printed texts or online resources that give factual information about a word or a topic. **Dictionaries**, **glossaries**, and **thesauruses** are examples of reference materials you can use to learn about words.

Dictionaries and Glossaries

Dictionaries and glossaries give lots of information about words. You can use a print or digital *dictionary* to look up any word that you would like to know more about. You can use a *glossary*, which is found in the back of a print book or as a link in an e-book (also called a digital book), to look up key words used in that book.

Entry

The words listed in a dictionary or glossary are called entries. They are in bold type and alphabetical order.

Pronunciation

An entry word is followed by its pronunciation, or the way it is spoken. The pronunciation is broken into syllables, and accent marks show which syllables to emphasize.

Part of Speech and Definitions

A word's part of speech and definitions follow its pronunciation. Multiple definitions are numbered, and the most common meanings are usually listed first.

Sample Sentences

Some dictionaries and glossaries give sample sentences so you can see how a word is used. Pictures may also be included to help you understand word meanings.

Sample Dictionary: Model

Look at the sample dictionary entry below. Note the entry word, the pronunciation, the part of speech, the definitions, and the sample sentences.

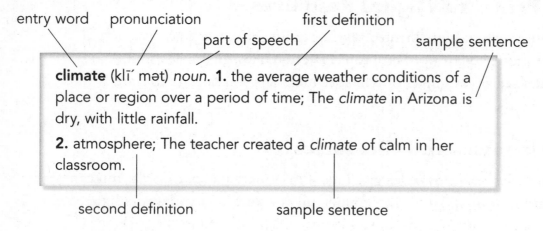

Now look at this glossary entry. You can see how similar it is to a dictionary entry. One difference is that the glossary entry includes the page number of where the word is located in the book. Another difference is that only the definition of the word as it is used in the book is included.

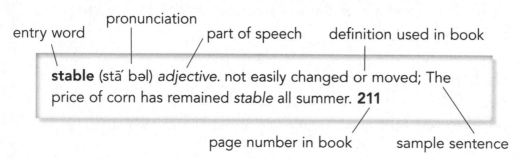

Now turn to pages 291–292 to practice using dictionary and glossary entries.

Name _____

Dictionaries and Glossaries

Practice

A. **Use the dictionary entry below to answer the questions. Write the correct letter on each line.**

> **nature** (nā chər) *noun.* **1.** the basic character of a person; Mom always tells the truth because it is not in her *nature* to be dishonest. **2.** the physical world, especially living things and objects such as rocks and air; Lily, Jake, and Noah love to study *nature* when they hike in the forest preserve.

1. Which definition of *nature* fits the meaning of the word as it is used in this sentence?

The woman's kindly nature led her to a career in animal rescue. _____

    a. Definition #1   **b.** Definition #2

2. True or false? The word *nature* rhymes with the word *stature* (stā chər). _____

    a. True   **b.** False

3. Which definition of *nature* is the one studied by naturalists? _____

    a. Definition #1   **b.** Definition #2

B. **Follow the steps below to find the word *amateur* in the glossary. Then answer the questions that follow.**

1. Type your *Common Core State Standards Literacy eHandbook* address into your browser's address bar.

2. Click on Part 6: Language in the first Table of Contents.

3. Go to 6.3 Vocabulary Acquisition and Use in the second Table of Contents.

4. Click on Use Print and Digital Resources.

5. Click on Dictionaries and Glossaries.

6. Click on Practice.

7. Click on the Digital Glossary button.

Name _____

1. Which part of speech for *amateur* is shown in this glossary entry?

_____

2. What are the entries above and below the word *amateur*?

_____

3. *Amateur* can also be used as a noun. Use *amateur* as a noun in a sentence of your own.

_____

_____

Thesauruses

A **thesaurus** is a reference book similar to a dictionary. Instead of giving definitions, however, a thesaurus lists **synonyms** for words. Synonyms are words that have the same (or nearly the same) meaning. In order to be considered synonyms, the words must be the same part of speech. For example, the words *abundant* and *plentiful* are synonyms.

Some thesauruses also include **antonyms** for words. Antonyms are words that have opposite meanings. In order to be considered antonyms, the words must be the same part of speech. For example, *abundant* and *scarce* are antonyms. Knowing synonyms for an unfamiliar word can help you understand and remember it.

These steps can assist you in using a print or digital thesaurus.

Use the thesaurus to look up the unfamiliar word, such as *abominable* in the sentences below. A thesaurus, like dictionaries and glossaries, lists words alphabetically.
- The weather was abominable last January.
- His playing was abominable in the final set of the championship match, so he lost.

Write down the synonyms for the word. You can use a chart to collect the information.

Unfamiliar Word	Synonyms
abominable	bad, terrible, awful, hateful, lousy, foul, offensive

Replace the unfamiliar word in the sentence with one of the synonyms you found. Read the sentence with the synonym to help you make sense of the meaning.
- The weather was foul last January.
- His playing was terrible in the final set of the championship match, so he lost.

Now turn to pages 294–295 to practice using a thesaurus.

6

Name _____

Thesauruses

Practice

Use a thesaurus to find synonyms for each boldfaced word. Write your synonyms in the T-chart. Then rewrite the sentence using a synonym that fits the sentence. The first one has been done for you.

1. There was a lot of **commotion** as the dog began chasing the cat around the house.

Unfamiliar Word	Synonyms
commotion	uproar, fuss, confusion, noise, excitement

Sentence with the synonym:
There was a lot of noise as the dog began chasing the cat around the house.

2. Jody's mother was **distressed** when she could not find a taxi to take her to the meeting.

Unfamiliar Word	Synonyms
distressed	

Sentence with the synonym:

_____

_____

Name _____

3. Miguel was known as **forthright;** you could always trust what he had to say.

Unfamiliar Word	Synonyms
forthright	

Sentence with the synonym:

_____

_____

Lesson E
Understand Figurative Language

Figurative language is language that goes beyond the literal, dictionary meaning of the words. Some examples of figurative language are called figures of speech. Writers use figures of speech to help create pictures in their readers' minds. In this lesson, you will learn about two figures of speech: **simile** and **metaphor**.

A simile compares two things that are not alike by using the words *like* or *as*. A metaphor compares two things that are not alike but without using *like* or *as*.

Similes

- Use the word *like* or *as* to signal the comparison

Example:

She moves on the tennis court like a dancer.

Both

- Compare two unlike things
- Help readers picture what is being described
- May relate unfamiliar things to familiar things

Metaphors

- State that one thing *is* the other; do not use *like* or *as*

Example:

She is a dancer on the tennis court.

Similes

A simile compares two unlike things using the connecting word *like* or *as*. Authors use similes to describe images or ideas that might otherwise be difficult to understand.

Here is an example of a simile:

> Whenever her grandmother visited, <u>the girl was like sugar.</u>

In this simile, the girl is being compared to sugar. Why would the author want to compare the girl to sugar? See how a student used a word web to better understand the meaning of the simile.

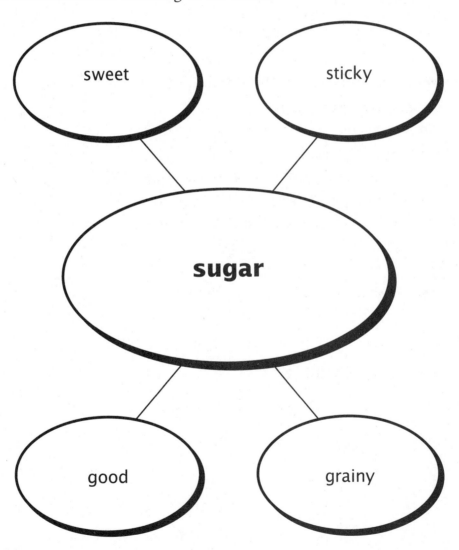

The author is saying that the girl was sweet and good whenever her grandmother visited.

Metaphors

A metaphor is a type of figurative language that compares two unlike things and shows how they are similar. Authors use metaphors to describe things and to make their writing more interesting. A metaphor states that one thing *is* the other.

To understand a metaphor, ask yourself these questions:

- What two things are being compared?
- What are the qualities of the two things?
- How is the writer saying that these two things are alike?

Here is an example of how to analyze and understand a metaphor.

The highway is an arrow across the state.

What two things are being compared?
the highway and an arrow

What are the qualities of the two things?
A highway is where cars drive, and an arrow can move straight.

How is the writer saying that these two things are alike?
The highway moves straight across the state, like an arrow that's been shot.

Now turn to pages 299–302 to practice understanding figurative language.

Name _____

Similes

Practice

A. Read the simile below and then answer the questions that follow.

The surface of the water was like glass.

1. What is the author comparing to glass? _____

2. Write the word *glass* in the center of the word web below. Then write four words or phrases you think of when you think of glass.

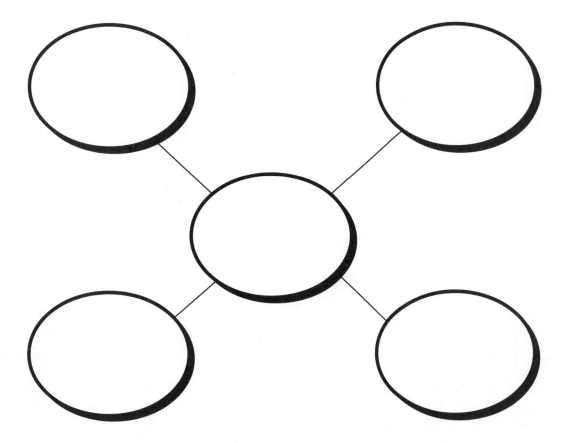

3. Explain what the author is trying to describe for the reader by using this simile.

_____

_____

Name _____

B. Follow the directions below.

1. Explain this simile in your own words: *The first time I went to summer camp* **I felt like a fish out of water,** *but now I look forward to it all year.*

_____

_____

2. Write your own sentence using this simile: *as quiet as a mouse.*

_____

_____

Name _____

Metaphors

Practice

A. Each of these sentences contains a metaphor. Answer the questions that follow each sentence.

1. During the whole crisis, the firefighter was a rock.

What two things are being compared? _____

What are the qualities of the two things? _____

How is the writer saying that these two things are alike?

_____

_____

2. In the morning, the snow was a blanket over the yard.

What two things are being compared? _____

What are the qualities of the two things? _____

How is the writer saying that these two things are alike?

_____

_____

3. The third base player was a wall in front of left field and did not let one ball get past her.

What two things are being compared? _____

What are the qualities of the two things? _____

How is the writer saying that these two things are alike?

_____

_____

Name _____

4. The ferocious wind was an animal howling and clawing at the window.

What two things are being compared? _____

What are the qualities of the two things? _____

How is the writer saying that these two things are alike?

_____

_____

B. Follow the directions below.

1. Explain this metaphor in your own words: *The colorful birds are jewels in the trees.*

_____

_____

2. Write your own sentence using a metaphor to relate the moon to a pearl.

_____

_____

Lesson F
Understand Common Expressions and Sayings

Idioms, adages, and proverbs are types of common expressions and sayings that have meanings beyond what can be understood by their individual words.

An **idiom** is an expression common to a particular culture that does not mean what it literally says. You have to learn the meanings of idioms, just like you learn the meanings of words. For example, the idiom *Break a leg!* means "Good luck!" People often say this to performers before a show.

A **proverb** is a statement of practical wisdom expressed in a simple way. An example of a proverb is "A stitch in time saves nine," which means that doing something in a timely way saves you from having to do more work later. An **adage** is a well-known proverb that has been used for a long time. An example of an adage would be "Where there's smoke, there's fire," which means that if there is evidence that something is happening, it probably is actually happening. Adages and proverbs are so closely related that the terms are often used interchangeably.

Idioms

There are different ways to figure out the meaning of an **idiom**. Sometimes you can figure out the meaning of an idiom using context clues, or familiar words around the idiom. In this example, the underlined words give clues to the meaning of the idiom *it takes two to tango*. *It takes two to tango* means "both sides are at fault in a conflict."

> Whenever they had a <u>conflict</u>, the twins agreed that it takes two to tango. Because they were <u>both at fault</u>, they often quickly forgave one another.

You may be able to understand the meaning of an unfamiliar idiom by focusing on just one of the words in the idiom. In the following idioms, the underlined word gives a clue to each idiom's meaning.

Drop **in the bucket** . . . means . . . **very small; not important**
Plain **as the nose on your face** . . . means . . . **obvious**

Sometimes an idiom can be found in a dictionary under its main word. For example, in the dictionary entry for *cut,* you can see that the idiom *cut corners* means "to do something in the quickest or easiest way."

If you cut corners when you do your homework, you won't learn your lessons well.

Finally, sometimes you just have to ask for the meaning of an idiom. Many idioms are used in everyday language, so you can memorize what they mean. One example of a common idiom is *spill the beans,* which means "tell a secret."

I knew my cousin was keeping a secret from me, so I told her to spill the beans.

Now turn to page 305 to practice using what you know about idioms.

Name _____

Idioms

Practice

A. Write the meaning of each idiom on the line.

1. walking on air _____

2. beat around the bush _____

3. all ears _____

4. land on one's feet _____

5. couch potato _____

6. heart of gold _____

7. cost an arm and a leg _____

B. Circle the meaning of the underlined idiom.

1. We have to tighten our belts and follow our budgets if we want to take a trip this year.

    a. be more careful with money   **b.** move the buckles over a notch

2. Looking for something in Brent's messy room is like searching for a needle in a haystack.

    a. something sharp and pointy   **b.** something hard to find

3. I was worried we wouldn't get to the game on time, but we arrived at the eleventh hour.

    a. at eleven o'clock   **b.** at the last minute

Adages and Proverbs

Adages and **proverbs** offer advice and observations about life. You can build your knowledge of adages and proverbs by asking someone what they mean or by looking them up online. Read these examples of adages and proverbs.

A watched pot never boils . . . means . . .
Things you look forward to seem to take a long time to happen.

You live, you learn . . . means . . .
Mistakes can teach useful lessons.

Don't bite the hand that feeds you . . . means . . .
Don't hurt those who take care of you, or they may not want to take care of you anymore.

Nothing ventured, nothing gained . . . means . . .
You can't expect to achieve something if you never even try to do it.

The early bird catches the worm . . . means . . .
If you start something early, you have a better chance of succeeding at it.

Now turn to pages 307–308 to practice using what you know about adages and proverbs.

Name _____

Adages and Proverbs

Practice

A. Underline the adage or proverb in each sentence, and then circle the correct meaning.

1. Although I was still mad at my cousin for losing my book, I decided to let sleeping dogs lie and not mention it again.

   a. It is better not to restart an old argument.

   b. It is better to let your relatives' pets sleep on the floor.

2. When I pack my lunch, I always tell myself that an apple a day keeps the doctor away.

   a. Telling doctors you eat an apple every day keeps them from scolding you.

   b. Eating an apple every day keeps you in good health.

3. Dad said that while the rest of us are out grocery shopping, he's going to make hay while the sun shines and take a nap.

   a. The best place to take a nap is outside in the sun.

   b. Take advantage of an opportunity while you have chance to do so.

4. When Danny asked his grandmother why she saved used wrapping paper, she replied, "Waste not, want not."

   a. If you carefully save things, you will not find yourself in need of things.

   b. If you don't want anything, you are not a wasteful person.

5. I didn't want to move to a different town, but every cloud has a silver lining; I made lots of friends at my new school.

   a. You can find interesting shapes in every cloud in the sky.

   b. You can find something good in every bad situation.

Name _____

B. Use your own words to explain what these common expressions mean.

1. Don't count your chickens before they're hatched.

_____

_____

2. A bird in the hand is worth two in the bush.

_____

_____

Lesson G
Understand Word Relationships

Understanding synonyms, antonyms, and homographs helps you build your vocabulary by relating new words to words you might already know. You can use a thesaurus to find synonyms—and often antonyms—for words. A dictionary is another tool for finding synonyms and antonyms, and it also shows you homographs.

Synonyms

Synonyms are words that have the same, or nearly the same, meaning. In order to be considered synonyms, two words must be the same part of speech. For example, in the sentence below, *apparatus* and *tool* are synonyms.

> The scientist used an <u>apparatus</u>, or <u>tool</u>, for testing the soil.

Read the following sentence. Note the underlined word.

> More than two-thirds of states need to <u>ratify</u> a treaty.

Look at the T-chart below. It has been used to list synonyms for the word *ratify*. Using a T-chart can help you find synonyms to understand and remember unfamiliar words.

Unfamiliar Word	Synonyms
Ratify	approve, authorize, confirm

Now read the sentence below. The word *ratify* has been replaced by a more familiar synonym, *approve*. You can replace an unfamiliar word with a synonym in the sentence to check that it makes sense in the sentence.

> More than two-thirds of states need to <u>approve</u> a treaty.

Turn to pages 310–311 to practice using what you know about synonyms.

Name _____

Synonyms

Practice

A. Each sentence has a synonym for the boldfaced word. Write it on the line.

1. My cleats were **encrusted,** or smeared, with dirt after the ball game.

_____

2. Studying can be fun when the **circumstances,** or conditions, of the work are pleasant.

_____

3. On the shelf were ten **fragile** vases made of breakable glass.

_____

4. The boy was **prohibited** from eating sweets before dinner to prevent him from spoiling his appetite.

_____

Name _____

B. **Read the passage. Use the T-chart to list synonyms for the boldfaced words. You may use a thesaurus or dictionary to help you. Then use the lines to rewrite the sentences, replacing each boldfaced word with the synonym that makes the most sense.**

> The most **valiant** person I ever knew was my friend Running Deer. Once, while we were hiking in the forest, we came across a mother bear and her cub. I was well behind my friend when we saw the pair. The mother growled in our direction. Running Deer stood up tall and yelled and waved his arms at the bears. I could only **speculate** as to what he was thinking! The mother bear and her cub turned and walked off through the brush.

Unfamiliar Word	Synonyms
valiant	
speculate	

Sentence 1: _____

_____

Sentence 2: _____

_____

Antonyms

Antonyms are words that have opposite meanings. In order to be antonyms, two words must be the same part of speech. Words like *but, not, on the other hand, instead of,* and *rather* often signal that an antonym might be used in the text. For example, in the sentence below, *immaterial* and *useful* are antonyms.

The map was <u>immaterial</u> and not <u>useful</u> at all in finding the buried treasure.

Read this passage to see how using antonyms can help you figure out what a word means.

Last year my family went to a national park for our vacation. We saw wild animals that we had seen only in books, and we were amazed by the landscape of trees and rivers. The highlight of the trip was an <u>arduous</u> hike we took to the top of a small mountain. Though the hike was not easy, due to all the loose rocks and exposed roots on the path, the spectacular view from the top was worth it!

You do not know the meaning of the underlined word. You look for clue words and notice the word <u>not</u>.

↓

You read the sentence that contains the word <u>not</u> and try to find an antonym.

↓

You see that easy is an antonym for <u>arduous</u> in this context.

↓

You now know that one meaning for <u>arduous</u> is "not easy."

Now turn to page 314 to practice using what you know about antonyms.

Name _____

Antonyms

Practice

A. Write at least three antonyms for each word in the chart below. You may use a thesaurus or a dictionary to help you.

Word	Antonyms
1. haughty	
2. veteran	
3. unique	
4. diminutive	
5. tense	

B. Read each sentence. Write the word from the sentence that is an antonym for the boldfaced word.

1. The broken glass clue was **significant** to the robbery investigation, not unimportant such as the footprint clue. _____

2. James was **passionate** about football, unlike his brother, who was uninterested in the sport. _____

3. The presentation by the nature guide was **engrossing,** not boring like we thought it would be. _____

4. There was no doubt that Emily needed to be more **audible** and less soft-spoken in her next presentation to the class. _____

5. Josie had a **conventional** style of dress, unlike her twin sister, who preferred unusual outfits. _____

Homographs

Homographs are words that are spelled the same but have different meanings and origins. They may also have different pronunciations and be different parts of speech. In the sentences below, *story* and *story* are homographs.

I visited the library on the third <u>story</u> of the building. While I was there, I read a <u>story</u> about the building's history.

While you might need a dictionary to check the pronunciations of homographs, often you can figure out the meanings by using context clues. Note the underlined homographs as you read the following sentences.

1. One way to make dried flowers is to <u>squash</u> them flat between the pages of a book.
Some Native American groups traditionally planted corn, beans, and <u>squash</u> together.

In the first sentence, "flat between the pages of a book" leads you to understand that *squash* is a verb meaning "press." The second sentence shows you that *squash* is also a noun naming a type of vegetable.

2. Mom <u>crooked</u> her arm to carry the bag of groceries.
Use a ruler to draw a line that is not <u>crooked</u>.

As you read the first sentence, think about what someone's arm looks like while carrying a bag. This gives you the clue that *crooked* is a verb that means "bent." In the second sentence, you can tell that *crooked* is an adjective that means "not straight" because you know that a line drawn with a ruler is straight.

3. If you have a <u>minute</u> to talk, I promise I won't take up a lot of your time.
I feel like just a <u>minute</u> part of the universe when I look up at the vast night sky.

In the first sentence, the fact that the speaker promises not to take up a lot of time gives you the clue that *minute* is a noun that means "moment." In the second sentence, as you think about how big the sky is and how small people are, you understand that *minute* here is an adjective meaning "tiny."

Now turn to page 316 to practice using what you know about homographs.

Name _____

Homographs

Practice

A. Read each sentence. Circle the definition of the underlined word as it is used in the sentence.

1. When is the deadline for the project?

   a. task　　　　　　　　　　　　**b.** throw forward

2. The moral of the story is to be kind to others.

   a. friendly and helpful　　b. the same type

3. The townspeople worked together to remove the refuse from the streets.

   a. turn down　　　　　　　　　**b.** trash

4. Seeing the sun after many days of rain never fails to entrance people.

   a. delight　　　　　　　　　　　**b.** the way inside

5. Put the cookies and muffins in separate containers

   a. keep apart; sort　　　　　　**b.** individual

B. Read the definitions for each homograph. Then write a sentence using each of the definitions.

1. tear

   a. moisture from an eye _____

   b. rip _____

2. palm

   a. inside of a hand _____

   b. type of tree _____

3. rest

   a. sleep _____

   b. what is left _____

Common Core State Standards Literacy Handbook

Lesson H
Build Vocabulary

As you read, you use vocabulary strategies to figure out the meanings of unfamiliar words. Once you understand new words, you can use them when writing and speaking.

The more carefully you choose your words and phrases, the more effective your descriptions will be.

Using Precise Language

Using precise language is important in expressing exactly what you mean. For example, an author who writes "the wolf *loped* through the forest" gives a clearer—and more interesting—description of that action than an author who writes "the wolf *moved* through the forest."

Using precise language helps your readers and listeners use their senses to imagine how something or someone looks, sounds, smells, tastes, or feels. When you choose your words, think about exactly what kind of information you want to give your readers or listeners. What do you want them to visualize?

Using Precise Language: Model

Study the examples below. Note how the changes give the reader a more precise picture of what is being described.

Original: The boy went home to tell his mother about the dog.

Revised: The boy went home <u>quickly</u> to tell his mother about the dog.

The author added an adverb to help the reader "see" how the boy went home.

Original: The train blew its whistle.

Revised: The train blew its <u>loud</u>, <u>shrill</u> whistle.

The author added adjectives to help the reader "hear" the train's whistle.

Original: Tania walked out of the gym after the game.

Revised: Tania <u>stomped</u> out of the gym after the game.

The author replaced the verb with a more precise synonym to better describe how Tania feels.

Now turn to pages 319–320 to practice using precise language.

Name _____

Using Precise Language

Practice

A. Read each word in the first column of the table below. Write three synonyms for each word. Then write three adjectives or adverbs that could be used to describe the word. The first one has been done for you

Word	Synonyms	Adjectives/Adverbs
run (verb)	jog, trot, dash	quickly, slowly, fast
jump (verb)		
laugh (verb)		
flower (noun)		
building (noun)		
person (noun)		

B. Read the story about an orange grove in Florida. Replace each of the boldfaced words with a more precise word that conveys the sense of urgency the writer is trying to express. Write the words on the lines that follow. You may use a dictionary or thesaurus to help you.

> That evening everyone was **very** quiet at dinner. Marisol **looked** around the table at each of her relatives, trying to figure out the mystery of what was upsetting them. Suddenly Uncle Carlos rose and touched the window with his hand, as if he were checking its temperature. Just then a man **came** through the door. Marisol recognized him as one of the workers from the orange grove.
>
> "Excuse me, sir!" the man said. "We've done what we can, and we're ready when you want to **look at** things."
>
> Uncle Carlos **left** his meal and **walked** from the house. After a moment, the other family members followed him. Juliana explained the situation to Marisol as they **moved** with the others toward the orange grove.

Name _____

> "Normally it's really hot in Florida, but sometimes in the winter the temperature drops," Juliana said, her voice quavering. "We've lost a lot of oranges the past few years, so we need a good season this year."
>
> "Oh, no!" Marisol now comprehended what her aunt and uncle had been whispering about earlier.
>
> As the group reached the first row of orange trees, Marisol saw that the **big** fans had been turned on and were whirring noisily. Sprinklers coated the oranges with water. If the temperature stayed at freezing for only a few hours, most of the oranges could be saved.

1. very _____

2. looked _____

3. came _____

4. look at _____

5. left _____

6. walked _____

7. moved _____

8. big _____

Using Content Words

You need to choose your words carefully when you are communicating about a particular topic. **Content words and phrases** are specific to a topic or course of study, and they give meaning to new concepts. For example, imagine you are discussing the topic of government. You might use words such as *constitution, democracy, amendment, ratify, repeal, economy, federal,* and *election* as you focus on this topic.

Think about how you use content words that are specific to each subject you study in school. For example, you learn in math class that the word *mean* means "average" and that the word *perimeter* refers to the boundary of a shape. In science class, you might learn that *climate* means "the average weather conditions of a place or region over a period of years" and that the *mantle* is a layer between the surface and the core of Earth. You read in social studies class that *emigrate* means "to leave one's country and live in another" and that *immigrate* means "to come into a new country to live in it."

Using Content Words: Model

Asking and answering questions is a strategy you can use to learn new words. When you come across an unfamiliar word, you might ask these questions: What is it? What are some of its properties? What is an example of it? If a text doesn't give you all of the information you need, you can use your own background knowledge or other reference materials to find the information. Read the following passage and apply this strategy to understand the word *nutrient*.

> Land plants include ferns, trees, flowers, and mosses. Almost all of these plants obtain their energy through the process of photosynthesis, during which they use the sun's energy to change carbon dioxide and water into foods such as starches and sugars. These nutrients provide much of what plants need to grow and reproduce.

nutrient	
What is it?	something needed by living things for life and growth
What are some of its properties?	Nutrients provide energy. Nutrients come from nature. Nutrients are found in food.
What is an example of it?	Starches and sugars are examples of nutrients.

Now turn to page 323–324 to practice using content words.

Name _____

Using Content Words

Practice

Read the passage below. Then use the strategy of asking and answering questions to help you better understand the boldfaced words. Write your answers in the charts.

> The oldest dinosaurs so far discovered are thought to have lived on Earth 230 million years ago. However, scientists are always on the lookout for **evidence** of even older **species.** Dinosaurs were a very successful life form; as a group, they lived on the planet for about 165 million years. Why did these animals ultimately become **extinct?** Several causes probably contributed to the end of the dinosaurs, but many scientists think the cause was the impact on Earth of a giant **asteroid** from outer space.

evidence	
What is it?	
What are some of its properties?	
What is an example of it?	

species	
What is it?	
What are some of its properties?	
What is an example of it?	

Name _____

extinct	
What is it?	
What are some of its properties?	
What is an example of it?	

asteroid	
What is it?	
What are some of its properties?	
What is an example of it?	

Using Words That Signal Relationships

Other words important to effective communication are **words that signal relationships** between ideas. These words help organize the flow of information in a logical way. For example, words such as *however, although,* and *nevertheless* tell you that one idea is different from another.

Using Words That Signal Relationships: Model

When you communicate, you need to organize your ideas. Your readers or listeners need to be able to make connections between ideas and topics.

Some words signal addition to an idea. These words let your audience know that more is about to be said on a topic. Study these examples of words that signal addition.

similarly	moreover	in addition
other	another	too
also	next	and

Other words signal contrast between ideas. Study the words below. Think about how these words can provide structure to a text.

however	although	nevertheless
but	yet	on the other hand
otherwise	in contrast	rather

Now turn to page 326 to practice using words that signal relationships.

Name _____

Using Words That Signal Relationships

Practice

Read the passage. Circle five signal words, using the charts on page 813 if you need help. Then use complete sentences to answer the questions.

> Terrance had been at Grandma's house for two hours. He was already bored. Terrance was used to city life; however, Grandma lived in the country. Although at home Terrance could walk to the baseball field by himself, here in the country Grandma had to drive him to the nearest one. Moreover, Grandma didn't even have a computer! Terrance was supposed to stay at Grandma's for a month, but he was sure it would feel like a year.
>
> Then Grandma showed Terrance a big plastic box full of old baseball cards. Terrance knew that he and Grandma were very different people; nevertheless, he could see that they were both big baseball fans. As they started to sort the cards, Grandma told Terrance stories about the players. Maybe summer at Grandma's would be fun after all!

1. What is one way that Terence and Grandma are different?

_____

_____

2. What is one way that Terence and Grandma are the same?

_____

_____

Common Core State Standards Literacy Handbook